Robert Adam and Kedleston

Robert Adam

The National Trust

and Kedleston

The Making of a Neo-Classical Masterpiece

by Leslie Harris, edited and with a foreword by Gervase Jackson-Stops

This catalogue, the exhibition's American tour, and conservation work on the drawings shown, have been made possible by a generous grant from Mr and Mrs Henry J. Heinz

All profits from the sale of the catalogue will go to the National Trust's Kedleston Hall Appeal, and further donations will be gratefully received by The Kedleston Appeal Manager, 36 Queen Anne's Gate, London SW1H 9AS, or the Executive Director, Royal Oak Foundation Inc., 41 East 72nd Street, New York, NY 10021

Designed by Derek Birdsall RDI
Made and Printed in Great Britain by
Balding + Mansell International Limited, Wisbech

ISBN 0 7078 0087 0

Cover illustration: *Design for the Painted Breakfast Room in the Family Pavilion*, by Robert Adam, 1760 (See Nos. 37–39)

Title page: *Robert Adam (1728–1792)*, attributed to George Willison (National Portrait Gallery, London)

Back cover: *Design for a Milestone or Milliarium*, by Robert Adam, 1760 (No. 78)

Contents

Foreword *by Gervase Jackson-Stops*

The north front

As one of the greatest of all English country houses, it was appropriate that Kedleston should be well represented in the recent *Treasure Houses of Britain* exhibition, held at the National Gallery of Art in Washington D.C. One of John Linnell's huge sofas from the Drawing Room, carved with near-life-size mermaids and tritons, crossed the Atlantic to become the largest single piece of furniture in the show; "Athenian" Stuart's tripod perfume-burner and Diederich Nicolaus Anderson's magnificent plate-warmer, from the Dining Room, formed the centre-piece of the 18th-century display of plate – dividing the earlier Rococo pieces from the later Neoclassical; and an early photograph of Lord Curzon of Kedleston as Viceroy of India, in a wonderfully carved ivory frame, evoked the splendour of the Raj in the final gallery. But perhaps the least-known, and most beautiful, of all the items lent from the house was an exquisite watercolour by Robert Adam, a design for a "Painted Breakfasting Room" (no. 41), that showed one of Britain's greatest architects at the height of his powers.

The great collection of architectural drawings at Kedleston – though one of the finest in any country house – has until now remained something of a hidden treasure, known only to a small circle of scholars. A few of them, like "Athenian" Stuart's designs for a "great room" (nos. 11–14) and Adam's design for the sideboard niche in the Dining Room (no. 15), have been published, and others have been shown from time to time in the Indian Museum below the Saloon at Kedleston. But the first serious study of the drawings, relating them to documents in the remarkably complete family archive, has been undertaken only in the last ten years by Mr Leslie Harris.

Mr Harris's researches into the history of the house

were begun as early as 1962, though gathering momentum after 1977 when he became Lord Scarsdale's honorary archivist. The immaculately ordered arrangement of the papers at Kedleston today, and the preservation of the drawings in such good condition, is entirely his achievement, and the National Trust is particularly fortunate in having secured his services as its special adviser on the property.

The present exhibition, one of the first ever to be devoted to a single country house, was conceived partly to help the National Trust's current Kedleston Appeal (which it is hoped will enable the Trust to save the house complete with all its contents), partly to show the public on both sides of the Atlantic what is probably the most comprehensive *corpus* of Adam's work outside the Soane Museum, and partly to prepare for a permanent display of the most important architectural drawings at the house itself. It will be some time before the last word on Kedleston is known, and although Mr Harris's catalogue entries for the drawings break much new ground, and correct many old misapprehensions, they should perhaps be viewed as an interim report, leading to his *magnum opus*, a fully detailed history of the house and its setting, now in course of preparation.

The National Trust's plans to acquire Kedleston, already well on the way to being achieved, are a fitting culmination to that history, since for most of the time since the house was built, it has been open to visitors – and successive generations of the Curzon family have treated it not as a strictly private preserve, but as a true "Temple of the Arts", dedicated to the enjoyment and edification of others. "Amicis et Sibi" – the 1st Lord Scarsdale's inscription, carved on the parapet of Adam's south front – is truer today than ever, though neither of them can have known just how many friends Kedleston would make in the succeeding 200 years.

Early visitors like the Duchess of Northumberland, George Montagu and Horace Walpole, have left us fascinating accounts of work still in progress on the completion of the state rooms, and Samuel Curwen, who came in 1777, recorded that "My Lady was at home

and remained to indulge us, as is customary among the great folks, with a sight of every part of the house. By a full length picture in the drawing room, she is an exquisitely fine figure and by the housekeepers' character of as amiable a disposition as her figure denotes" (Oliver, 353). Such a description could almost have been written by a country-house visitor today, as could another episode in his narrative where "the eldest daughter of the Family going in a loose country dress to take a ramble over the lawn, on discovering us hastily retreated back, and disappeared".

The housekeeper referred to by Curwen was Mrs Garnett, the same "well-drest elderly Housekeeper, a most distinct Articulator . . .", who took Boswell and Johnson round the house only a few months later (Pottle, 31). Her portrait by Thomas Barber of Nottingham, still hangs in the house, and shows her holding a copy of the printed Kedleston catalogue,

The south front

which she would give to her charges. The earliest known copies of this guide (presumably written by the 1st Lord Scarsdale) date from 1769, and at least four further editions were published before 1800, with another four appearing in the 19th century. The Kedleston Inn on the north-eastern boundary of the park, designed by Adam in 1760–62, was built to serve the Bath House near the centre lake (a kind of miniature spa, see no. 80), but must also have done a good trade catering to the visiting gentry, drawn either by culture or mere curiosity to see this new rival to Chatsworth, the "Palace of the Peak".

If, as Mark Girouard claims, Kedleston was consciously built as a Tory "power house" to compete with its Whig neighbour, Chatsworth, the Curzon family estates were never a match for the vast territorial possessions of the Cavendishes – particularly after the gambling debts run up by the 2nd Lord Scarsdale, and the intestacy of the 3rd. That (and the conservatism of its later owners) may have accounted for its miraculous survival in the 19th century, when so many other great houses were altered or remodelled beyond recognition. But it might have sealed its fate in the 20th, had it not been for the fortune brought by Mary Leiter, the American first wife of Marquess Curzon of Kedleston, Viceroy of India.

The Marquess, the most distinguished in the long line of Curzons stretching back to the Norman Conquest, was one of the most influential early supporters of the National Trust, personally superintending the restoration of Bodiam Castle in Sussex and Tattershall in Lincolnshire (both of which he gave to the Trust), and helping to restore Montacute in Somerset. His death in 1925 came before the establishment of the Trust's Country Houses Scheme, however, and the crippling capital taxes levied then and on the death of his nephew, the 2nd Viscount Scarsdale, meant that Kedleston once more became a serious burden to its owners.

At long last a solution to this problem is now in sight. The house and park have very generously been offered as a gift to the National Trust by the present

Lord Scarsdale, and his steadfast determination to secure their future, during years of difficult negotiation, has finally prompted the government, through the National Heritage Memorial Fund, to offer an unprecedented sum towards the saving of Kedleston. The Trust still needs to raise £2 million by appeal so that it can secure all the original contents of the house, and have enough funds to carry out necessary restoration work – but it is confident that it can do so, with the help of its many supporters in Britain and in the United States.

The drawings shown here represent not only one of the crucial elements of the collection that the Trust has yet to save, but also precious documentary evidence for the restoration work that it would like to carry out: from the replacement of Adam's cresting on the Library bookshelves (nos. 29–32), to the reinstatement of his dazzling buffet display in the Dining Room (nos. 15–16), or the repair of his Fishing Room-Boathouse on the upper lake (nos. 67–69) – surely one of the most enchanting garden-buildings in Europe. Above all, they show just what is at stake – a Neo-classical masterpiece by one of Britain's very greatest architects, a treasure of international value that none of us can afford to lose.

The National Trust is deeply grateful to Mr and Mrs Henry J. Heinz for so generously sponsoring the restoration of the drawings (through the Trust's paper conservator, Miss Mary Goodwin) and the publication of this catalogue, and also making possible the exhibition's American tour. Lord and Lady Scarsdale and the Trustees of the National Heritage Memorial Fund have given every support to the project, and Mr Leslie Harris has of course been its inspiration and mainstay. The Trust is also grateful to Mr Derek Birdsall, Mr Howard Colvin, Mrs Maggie Grieve, Mr John Hardy, Mr John Harris, Dr Peter Leach, Mr C.H. Lucas, CBE, Miss Jane Preger, Mrs Margaret Richardson, Miss Nathalie Rothstein, Mr Michael Snodin and Mr Peter Thornton, for their assistance in a variety of ways.

Mrs. Garnett, Housekeeper at Kedleston,
by Thomas Barber of Nottingham, c.1800.
She is shown holding a copy of the Kedleston catalogue

Kedleston and the Curzons *by Leslie Harris*

Nathaniel Curzon, 1st Lord Scarsdale,
and his wife, Lady Caroline Colyear,
by Nathaniel Hone, 1761

We do not know exactly how long the Curzons have been at Kedleston, but probably from at least 1150, and certainly from 1198/99, during the reign of Richard Coeur de Lion. It was then that Richard de Curzun of the senior branch of the family made a grant to Thomas de Curzun of "all the vill of Ketelestune with the advowson of the church . . .". Successive generations added modestly to the property, but it was in the hundred years after 1650 that the estate grew to nearly 10,000 acres, with properties in Derbyshire and the surrounding counties of Leicestershire, Nottinghamshire and Staffordshire, as well as in London. By judicious management and a fairly modest life-style, income had risen to approaching £10,000 per annum in 1759; rentals were certainly over £7000.

The last of the senior branch of the family had died in 1645. Mary Curzon, Countess of Dorset, had been governess to the future James II and to Mary, his sister, Princess of Orange and mother of the future King William III. The Kedleston Curzons then became the senior branch, as they are today, one of the few English families directly descending in the male line from Norman ancestors. At almost the same time in 1636, John Curzon became a baronet of Scotland, and in 1641 of England. Sir John began the serious process of enlarging the estates referred to above, and it was these resources which were to enable the present great house to be built.

Our knowledge of the earlier generations of Curzons is limited, but during the Commonwealth period Sir John was on the Parliamentary side. A century later, during the 1745 Jacobite rising, when Bonnie Prince Charlie was to reach Derby, a subscription list of the gentlemen of Derbyshire was compiled in order to "defend our excellent Constitution in Church & State". It recorded Sir Nathaniel Curzon (father of the 1st Lord Scarsdale) making the second highest subscription, next to that of the Duke of Devonshire, the Lord Lieutenant of the County – more usually on opposite sides of the political arena. Of succeeding generations Nathaniel Curzon, 1st Lord Scarsdale, not only built Kedleston, but was Chairman of

Committees of the House of Lords from 1775–1789. For sheer length of possession his great-grandson Alfred Nathaniel, 4th Baron, must hold the record of sixty years from 1856 to 1916. His eldest son George Nathaniel, who became Viceroy of India, Foreign Secretary, and Marquess Curzon of Kedleston, was without doubt the most brilliant and celebrated member of the family.

Information about the various houses which preceded the present one is scanty. The advowson of the church (the right to appoint the parson) was included in the 1198–99 grant. The Norman church was largely rebuilt in the fourteenth century, but surviving Norman features suggest a date of about 1150; presumably there would also have been a manor house at this date. Fifteen generations of Curzons up to Sir John (who inherited in 1632) must have rebuilt this house from time to time, though probably always on the same site near the church. The first of which we have any knowledge was a late Elizabethan hall-plan house of about 1600. Of the red-brick Queen Anne house built around 1700 we have a plan (no. 51) and it also appears in a painting (no. 50). It was this house that Nathaniel Curzon inherited, as 5th Baronet, in November 1758: although quite sizeable, it was out-of-date, and he was ready and prepared to replace it. By 1761, when he was created 1st Baron Scarsdale, he had already started to construct a house whose size would be worthy of a peer of the realm – rather than a mere country squire.

No evidence has been found to show that Nathaniel Curzon made the usual Grand Tour, although in 1749 he made a brief journey in France, Belgium and Holland, which lasted just one month and cost £300 including the purchases he made. If this limited experience cannot be compared with Lord Burlington's two visits to Italy, or Lord Leicester's six years of Continental travel, there can be little doubt that Curzon was as imbued with the culture of the Mediterranean as they, and that he was personally responsible for the creation of Kedleston, in much the same way as Burlington and Leicester provided the ideas for Chiswick and Holkham – leaving professionals like Kent and Brettingham to provide the detail, and bring them to reality.

There is an excellent collection of architectural books at Kedleston, which seems to have begun during the latter part of the 17th century, and continued through the 18th. These volumes had a major influence on the young Curzon, who continued to expand the collection and they give interesting clues to his changing tastes: for instance the copies of Borromini's *Opera* of 1720 and *Opus* of 1725, which he bought in 1758, must soon have been discarded as too old-fashioned and Baroque, for they do not appear in his library catalogue of 1765.

The new house was designed to have five main components – the large central block facing north and south, with state rooms on the principal floor, were to be linked to four pavilions by quadrant corridors. The new central block was roughly to occupy the site of the old house. In the event only the two pavilions attached to the north (entrance) front were built.

Curzon inherited in November 1758 and only a month later Brettingham went to Kedleston to measure up, and presumably set out as far as practicable, the outline plan of the north pavilions and quadrants. The clutter of old brick and half-timbered out-buildings (see no. 50) were quickly demolished, and the family and kitchen pavilions were begun. The former was built under Brettingham's direction, and the latter under Paine. It has long been held that Paine designed and began the central block, including the north front, and that by the time Adam took charge, the building was too far advanced for him to make material alterations, though he was in time to redesign the south front. This sequence of events would have required the building to have progressed from north to south, but correspondence, accounts and drawings all prove that it grew from east to west, and that Adam would have had ample time to make serious changes to the north front had he or Lord Scarsdale decided to do so.

The first stage was to demolish the eastern third of the old house (seen on the right in no. 50) and in its place to build that part of the new house which

The Drawing Room

contains the present music room, drawing room and library. Paine began this work, but part had to be taken down and rebuilt. By April 1760, Adam was in complete charge of the central block, and also had considerable influence on the interiors of the pavilions (see nos. 37–39).

The north front, glimpsed through the trees when descending the drive from the lodge, is fully revealed on crossing (or pausing on) the bridge. It is, without doubt, the grandest Palladian façade in Britain, and with few rivals anywhere in the world. The central block, with its hexastyle portico and supporting double stairs, is derived from Colen Campbell's Wanstead (c.1714–20), but it is the perspective given by the pavilions, simple in themselves, which is so overwhelmingly impressive. As with its three most important predecessors, Houghton and Holkham in Norfolk, and Nostell Priory in Yorkshire, the plan with four pavilions stems from that of the unbuilt Villa Mocenigo, which Palladio illustrated in his *Quattro Libri* (2nd book, plate 58).

On the south front the lack of the intended pavilions and quadrants must be regretted, but the main block is still an elevation in depth, well expressing Adam's return to "movement" in architecture – "the rise and fall, the advance and recess with other diversity of form, in the different parts of a building, so as to add greatly to the picturesque of the composition". In simple terms it combines the Arch of Constantine with the Pantheon-like rotunda behind, just as the Roman Pantheon itself is approached through a Corinthian portico or temple-front. But in contrast with the static effect of many ancient Roman buildings, the forward thrust of the columns, with the entablature breaking out over them, the receding curve of the dome and the advancing curve of the horseshoe staircase and perron, give the south front of Kedleston a truly Baroque exuberance – best seen from the south-west in the morning, with the sun casting deep shadows on the stonework and highlighting the great statues high on the parapet.

The internal planning of the house is a combination of Roman domestic architecture (with ideas taken from Pliny's famous villa, reconstructed by Robert Castell in his *Villas of the Ancients* as early as 1728) with elements of the palaces, temples and baths which Adam had measured and drawn during his time in Italy. The monumental hall and saloon on the central axis – what Mark Girouard has called the "state centre" of the 18th-century country house plan – continue the huge scale and giant classical orders of the centrepieces to the two main fronts. In the 1769 edition of the Kedleston catalogue, Lord Scarsdale describes them as "the Greek Hall and Dome of the Ancients, proportioned chiefly from the Pantheon at Rome, and from Spalatra".

To the east of this central axis, the Music Room, Drawing Room and Library respectively represent the arts of music, painting and literature. If their common theme is recreation, the balancing state rooms on the west are devoted to hospitality: the "principal apartment" (Ante Room, Dressing Room, State Bedchamber, and Wardrobe) for the use of the most important guests, and the Dining Room, linked to the kitchen pavilion by the north-east quadrant corridor. Other guest rooms (the so-called "semi-state rooms") lay on the upper floor of the main block, while the family apartments lay, as they still do, in the north-east pavilion, linked to the Music Room by the second quadrant corridor.

The interior decoration of the rooms, whether in plasterwork, stone, marble, scagliola or carved wood, was of the very highest quality, usually executed by artists and craftsmen from working drawings produced in Adam's studio (see no. 48). The plastering firm of Joseph Rose was responsible for all the ceilings and other plasterwork in the state rooms. The stone-carver, William Collins, was, however, the modeller of the two plaster medallions in the Dining Room (see nos. 19–20). The scagliola pilasters in the Saloon came from the London workshop of Domenico Bartoli, while the decorative paintings inset in the ceiling of the Dining Room and the walls of the Hall and Saloon were contributed by two artists also habitually employed by Adam – Antonio Zucchi and Biagio Rebecca – together with William Hamilton and

The Marble Hall

Henry Morland, better known respectively as history and portrait painters.

The carving in wood and stone was carried out by a team of twelve craftsmen headed by James Gravener. As well as doors, doorcases, chair rails, shutters and other fittings, they made several important pieces of furniture such as the curved sideboards and pedestals in the Dining Room niche (to Adam's design), the large mahogany writing-desk in the centre of the Library, and the state bed with its curious end-posts carved to resemble full-size palm trees. The latter may (like the great palm-branch mirror in the State Dressing Room) have been inspired by a much earlier set of chairs with similar foliage, which Lord Scarsdale's father acquired about 1740, possibly from William Bradshaw. Another celebrated firm of London cabinet-makers, William and John Linnell, supplied many of the finest pieces in the house in the 1760s and '70s, including the card-tables and sofas in the Drawing Room (see no. 27), the settees with curved backs made for the niches of the Saloon, and very probably the remarkable set of benches in the Hall, based on an antique sarcophagus.

The picture collection at Kedleston is of great importance, not only remaining almost exactly as it was in the 1st Lord Scarsdale's time, but also hung on the walls in very much the same arrangement described in early catalogues. Lord Scarsdale must have inherited at least a hundred pictures from his predecessors including Lely and Kneller portraits; he might have acquired a number of small pictures during his month abroad in 1749; and at London sales between 1753 and 1759 he bought upwards of fifty, including the beautiful Cuyp, now in the Drawing Room, for 95 guineas. His agent, William Kent (a picture dealer, not to be confused with the architect of the same name), purchased thirty in Italy for about £2000, and Lord Scarsdale commissioned about thirty more from contemporary artists including Gavin Hamilton (in Rome), Nathaniel Hone, Joshua Reynolds and Francesco Zuccarelli. Some of his swans have turned out geese – his two Rembrandts are now given to followers of the master, and his Raphael has also been

demoted – but the Neapolitan and Bolognese *seicento* pictures, such as the great Giordano *Triumph of Bacchus* in the Music Room and the pair of Lutis in the Drawing Room, are splendid examples of their kind, representing a characteristic Augustan taste. Lord Scarsdale also arranged his pictures with thought and care, as can be seen from "Athenian" Stuart's and Robert Adam's wall elevations – where they are either named or sketched in – and Adam's fixed plasterwork frames for some of the canvases in the Music Room, and all of those in the Dining Room, have ensured (as he probably intended) that future generations could not tamper with the hanging.

The sculpture collection was of relatively minor importance as regards individual pieces, nearly all of them being plaster casts or copies of celebrated antique statues. But gathered together in the Saloon, where they remained until 1787–89 (when they were removed to the Hall and Staircase), they constituted a major innovation, following Lord Leicester's sculpture gallery at Holkham. The figures consisted of twelve casts which Lord Scarsdale had acquired by 1758 from the younger Matthew Brettingham, and the sculptors Richard Hayward and Joseph Wilton. Chimneypieces were of considerable importance; several were designed by Adam, and the tablets and figures carved by Wilton and the Dane, Michael Henry Spang.

The deer park and pleasure grounds were the essential setting of a great 18th-century mansion, and it was initially these, rather than the house, which Nathaniel Curzon asked the young Robert Adam to take in hand in December 1758 (see no. 61). Over the next twenty years, the landscape at Kedleston was changed out of recognition: the scattered village was moved to a new site west of the park; Charles Bridgeman's geometrical canals and ponds, made for the 3rd Baronet (see nos. 52–53), were transformed into serpentine lakes; and his formal gardens to the south of the house were swept away to create a "natural landscape", dotted with temples and garden buildings, all in the new Neo-classical taste.

Although the landscape gardener William Emes

began work at Kedleston as early as 1756, continuing to be employed up to 1760, Adam must have had an important influence, particularly in the layout of the pleasure grounds to the west and south-west of the house. The Long Walk here was already being laid out in the spring of 1760, and the complete lists for its planting, including laburnums, syringas, lilacs, honeysuckles, jasmine, broom and many other species of flowering and fragrant trees and shrubs, make fascinating reading. Most of the plants were supplied by the London nurseryman James Scott, and by Charles Sandys of Ashbourne, whose brother(?) John – the gardener at Kedleston – received a packet from Lord Scarsdale in 1763 containing the seeds of a "scarce Italian shrub called Rodo Dendrone".

Adam's garden buildings at Kedleston include the North Lodge with its triumphal arch and the new village entrance lodges, the bridge and cascade, and the Fishing Room on the upper lake with a cold bath and boathouses below it – while the hexagonal summerhouse was built by George Richardson in the 1770s, followed by the orangery in 1800.

All in all, Kedleston demonstrates the width of Robert Adam's range – as architect, garden designer and decorator – better than any of his other single country-house commissions. That it has survived, so little altered over the last two hundred years, is a tribute not only to his genius, and the vision shown by his patron, but also to the love and devotion it has inspired in the 1st Lord Scarsdale's descendants, who have cherished and maintained it over many generations.

Chronological Table

c.1700   Red-brick house built for Sir Nathaniel Curzon, 2nd Baronet, by Francis Smith of Warwick

1722–26   Charles Bridgeman laying out formal gardens for Sir John Curzon, 3rd Bt.

c.1726   James Gibbs' unexecuted designs for garden pavilions, and a new house

1756   William Emes begins work on park for Nathaniel Curzon (employed until April 1760)

1757–58   "Athenian" Stuart producing designs for Curzon, who succeeds as 5th Baronet (November 1758)

1758   Robert Adam's first meeting with Sir Nathaniel Curzon (December)

Matthew Brettingham and Jason Harris at Kedleston measuring the old house (December)

1759   Adam's first visit to Kedleston (?April)

Bath House in the park being constructed by Jason Harris (July); work continuing until 1761

Demolition of the east part of the old house, and clearing ground for new building; family pavilion built under Brettingham's direction; kitchen pavilion and quadrant corridors begun by James Paine

1759–60   Temporary stables and coach houses built by Jason Harris

Pleasure Grounds with Long Walk laid out and planted; ice house built

1760   Adam in charge of main block (from April?), and designs Painted Breakfast Room in family pavilion

1760–61   North Lodge built to Adam's design

1761   Fitting up of interiors of pavilions, and eastern part of main block; demolition of remaining section of old house (September)

1762   Foundations laid for centre and west parts of new main block (February); new offices built

Fosse (or ha-ha) constructed in Pleasure Grounds

1763   Completion of north portico, south front, Music Room and Drawing Room; alabaster columns erected in the Hall

Bentley Well built to Adam's design

1764   Stone staircases to north and south fronts built; skylights installed in Hall and Saloon; Library completed

1765   General completion of structure; completion of Dining Room; limited completion of Hall and Saloon; John Linnell's sofas for the Drawing Room arrive at the house

1768   Completion of the "Principal Apartment" (Ante Room, Dressing Room, State Bedchamber and Wardrobe). Adam's unexecuted designs for one-bay pavilions flanking the south front. Stables built by Samuel Wyatt, partially based on Adam's earlier design

1770–71   Bridge and cascade built to Adam's design

1770–72   Fishing Room (with cold bath and boathouses below) built to Adam's design

1770–75   Centre and lower lakes created

1775–78   Completion of Marble Hall to designs by George Richardson; Hexagon Temple (or Summerhouse) built(?)

1777   Visit of Johnson and Boswell

1787–89   Completion of Saloon (statues moved to Hall and Staircase)

Owners of Kedleston from 1700

Sir Nathaniel Curzon, 2nd Baronet (1635–1718)
   m. 1671 Sarah, daughter of William Penn

Sir John Curzon, 3rd Bt. (c.1674–1727)
   died unmarried, succeeded by his brother

Sir Nathaniel Curzon, 4th Bt. (1675–1758)
   m. 1716 Mary, daughter of Sir Ralph Assheton, 2nd Bt.

Nathaniel, 5th Bt., and (1761) 1st Baron Scarsdale (1726–1804)
   m. 1750 Caroline, daughter of the 2nd Earl of Portmore

Nathaniel, 2nd Baron Scarsdale (1751–1837)
   m. 1777 Sophia, daughter of the 1st Viscount Wentworth

Nathaniel, 3rd Baron Scarsdale (1781–1856)
   died unmarried, succeeded by his nephew

Rev. Alfred Nathaniel, 4th Baron Scarsdale (1831–1916)
   m. 1856 Blanche, daughter of Joseph Pocklington Senhouse

George Nathaniel, 5th Baron and 1st Viscount Scarsdale, Earl (1911) and (1921) Marquess Curzon of Kedleston (1859–1925)
   m. (1) 1895 Mary, daughter of Levi Leiter
     (2) 1917 Grace, daughter of J. Monroe Hinds
   died without male heirs, succeeded by his nephew.

Richard Nathaniel, 6th Baron and 2nd Viscount Scarsdale (1898–1977)
   m. (1) 1923 Mildred, daughter of William Roland Dunbar
     (2) 1946 Ottilie, daughter of Charles Pretzlik
   died without male heirs, succeeded by his cousin

Francis John Nathaniel, 7th Baron and 3rd Viscount Scarsdale (b. 1924)
   m. (1) 1948 Solange, daughter of Oscar Ghislain Hause
     (2) 1968 Helene, daughter of William Ferguson Thomson

A Note on the Heading and Dating of Adam drawings

In any study of the work of Robert Adam, the drawings by him, his brothers and other members of his office in the Soane Museum are of vital importance. Detailed examination of those drawings relating to Kedleston has suggested that headings, dates and other wording may occasionally be seriously misleading, or even mistaken. When dates are critical in comparing the sequence of operations, in matching the work of contemporary architects, or in tracing Adam's development it can be important to make use of other supporting documentary sources whenever they are available and firmly dated.

An example of an incorrect heading occurs in the two Soane Museum drawings (40:56, 57) of the elevation of a proposed pheasant house at Kedleston which were pasted side by side in the volume, with the heading ''Elevation and Plans of a Parsonage House at Keddleston for Lord Scarsdale''. However, there are two drawings at Kedleston for the same building entitled ''Design of a New Front for the Pheasant House at Kedleston'', signed and dated 1760. In the Museum there is also a simple drawing (9:104) for the actual parsonage house as built. It is noted at the foot ''Sketch of Parsonage House'', but with no location. The drawing had been submitted from Kedleston for Adam to ''improve'' by adding a pediment and other features.

Other misleading inscriptions appear on drawings (25:76–93) of the splendid silver fountains and cisterns, the chestnut vases, tripod, plate warmer and even the large jasper wine cooler (several of which were actually designed by ''Athenian'' Stuart). These drawings were noted at the foot ''For Sir Nathl Curzon Baronet''. In reality they had been drawn by one of Adam's draughtsmen to enable him to design the dining room alcove (see no. 16), and they had certainly not been designed by Adam. At this time, about 1761, the pieces were all stored at the Curzons' London house.

Many of the unsigned drawings in the Soane Museum are office copies in various stages of completion, including rough sketches and freehand designs. Many have been dated, usually in the bottom right hand corner in an ordinary (not copper-plate) hand, with a marked slant. Presumably these dates were added at some later time, probably before 1833 when the collection was bought from the family by Sir John Soane, and the volumes were put together.

In relation to Kedleston the dates generally seem about right, but there are minor variations in both directions. The finished drawing for the Music Room ceiling, still at the house, was signed and dated 1760 (see no. 21), but the incomplete drawing in the Soane Museum (11:57) was dated 1761. In the reverse direction the finished coloured drawing at Kedleston for the dining room ceiling was signed and dated 1762, whereas an unfinished office copy (11:53), also in colour, was dated 1761.

A whole group of ceiling drawings for Admiral Boscawen at Hatchlands were dated 1759 in the slanting figures, which may be correct. There are parallels to Kedleston designs, but complete reliance to a year could be misleading when comparing early events at this critical stage of Adam's development. Such houses as Hatchlands, Shardeloes, Harewood and Croome were all being built during these years, at the same time as Kedleston.

Dates on ''finished'' drawings can also raise problems. Adam produced a comprehensive set of drawings for most of the state rooms at Kedleston. The wall elevations for the Music Room were signed and dated 1760, but they show the pictures in their final positions after 1763 (excluding the organ wall). There is a similar situation with the Library, where the east wall is shown with the bookcase completely filling it (no. 30). In 1760 this would have been impossible because access to the south-east quadrant would have required a door. Hence the actual production of the drawings must be after the southern pavilions had been abandoned, which would date them c.1765 – although in general they are based on the designs of 1760.

The Catalogue: Note to the Reader

Dimensions given for the drawings are in inches, height before width. Inscriptions are given, within each entry, only where they are of some importance, and not clearly visible in the illustration.

Drawings given to Robert Adam should be understood as emanating from his office, and thus produced by carefully supervised draughtsmen (such as Agostino Brunias; see nos. 17 and 37–39), rather than being in Adam's own hand. The exceptions to this rule are the freely drawn landscapes and other rough sketches (such as nos. 61–66), which are entirely his.

1
"Plans & Uprights of Kedleston House"
after 1768
binding marbled board, red morocco label
with gilt lettering
supporting leaves with a variety of
watermarks JW, LVG
$11\frac{1}{2} \times 19\frac{3}{4}$

Most of the architectural drawings at
Kedleston were re-mounted in albums in
the 19th century, or have remained loose in
the library and (latterly) the archive room.
This binding, from which the drawings
have been removed, is the only original
18th-century example in the collection: six
drawings were pasted in, of which three are
exhibited (nos.7,8,9), while a number of
others were kept loose between the blank
pages.

2
Design for a House of Thirteen Bays c.1726
attributed to James Gibbs
pen, ink and wash
$10\frac{3}{4} \times 18$

James Gibbs was rebuilding All Saints Church, Derby (now the Cathedral) in 1723–25, and Sir John Curzon, 3rd Bart, contributed £50 to the works in 1723. Gibbs provided a design for two garden pavilions for Curzon published in his *Book of Architecture* of 1728 (plate 70), although, according to the text, their "execution was prevented by Sir John's death" in 1727. Ten guineas were paid to the architect in the Kedleston accounts for September, 1726, and this payment may possibly have been for drawings for the house as well as garden buildings.

The existing house at Kedleston, designed by Smith of Warwick, with a façade about 105 feet long, would have been little more than twenty years old and reasonably up-to-date. Whether Sir John, a Tory gentleman and a bachelor, would

have asked for an elevation 157 feet long in the 1720s, or whether Gibbs was presenting him with an unsolicited scheme, remains uncertain. The resemblance to two other unexecuted designs of the 1720s, for Sacombe Park in Hertfordshire, and Kirkleatham Hall in Yorkshire – all of them variants on the Palladian theme of the giant engaged portico – make it unlikely that the design was made any later than 1730. The cartouche in the pediment also recalls the east end of St. Martin-in-the-Fields, completed by October 1726.

In 1727–28 Gibbs designed steps to the main entrance at nearby Calke Abbey for Sir John Harpur, another contributor to the works at All Saints, Derby.

Literature: Friedman, 130–131, fig.133

3
Design for an Entrance Hall 1726
attributed to James Gibbs
pen, ink and watercolour
$14\frac{1}{2} \times 20\frac{1}{4}$

The draughtsmanship, the scale, and the measurements inscribed on the plan and elevations, are all typical of Gibbs and can be compared with his drawings at the Ashmolean, including interiors like the hall at Ditchley (Friedman, fig.119).

This drawing would presumably have been made about the same time as Gibbs' elevation (no.2). But the latter has an arched central doorcase, and this design seems more likely to be an adaptation of the hall in the old Smith of Warwick house (28 feet 9 inches wide, as opposed to 28 feet here, see no.51). What is of the greatest interest is Gibbs' proposal for a two-storey space, filled with sculpture, and with giant columns of the Corinthian order – which were all to be features of the Marble Hall as designed by Adam nearly forty years later (no.43). A copy of the famous Uffizi *Wrestlers* (as shown here) was acquired by the 1st Lord Scarsdale in 1757, but many earlier versions of it were made (by Jan Van Nost and others) and it is not surprising to find Gibbs using it as one of the models for the statuary here. Another cast of a well-known antique statue, the *Faun with Pipes* from the Villa Borghese (now in the Louvre) is shown in the niche at the bottom of the staircase.

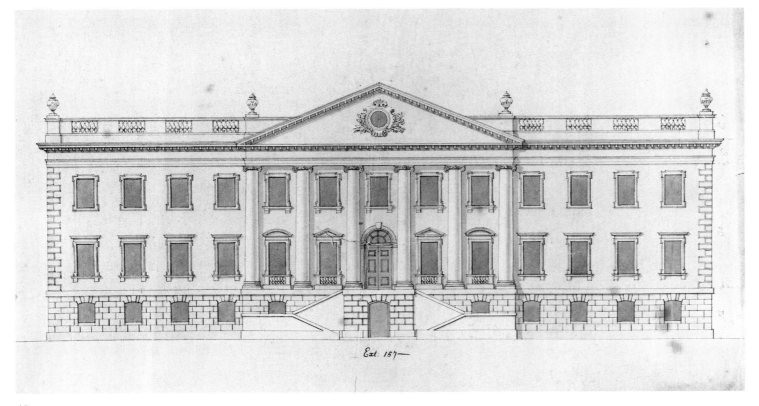

Ext. 157

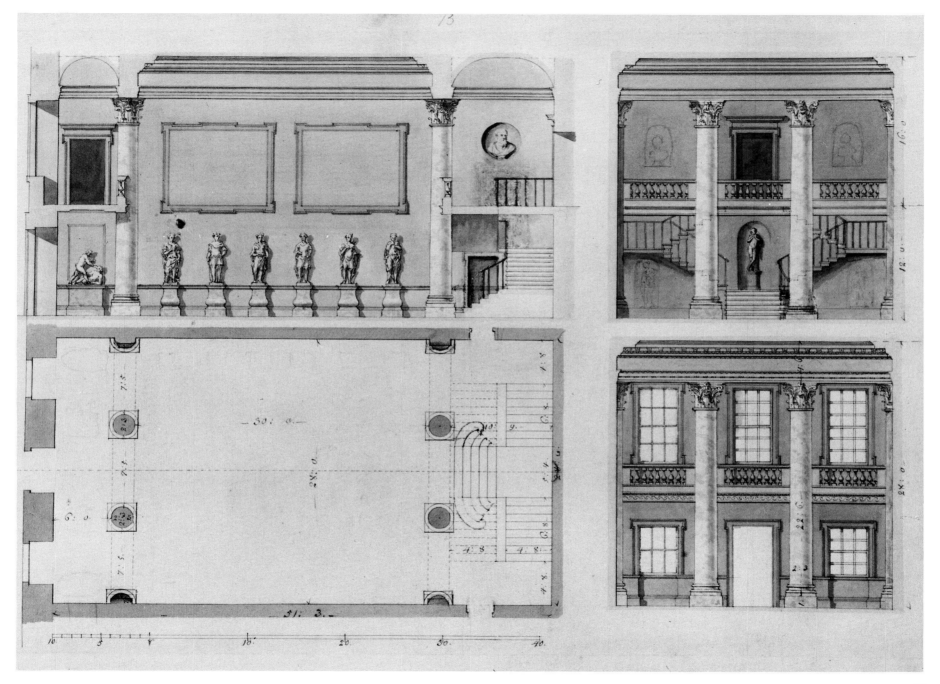

4
Design for the Family and Kitchen Pavilions c.1757–58
attributed to Matthew Brettingham the elder
pen, sepia ink and wash
$11\frac{1}{2} \times 17\frac{1}{2}$

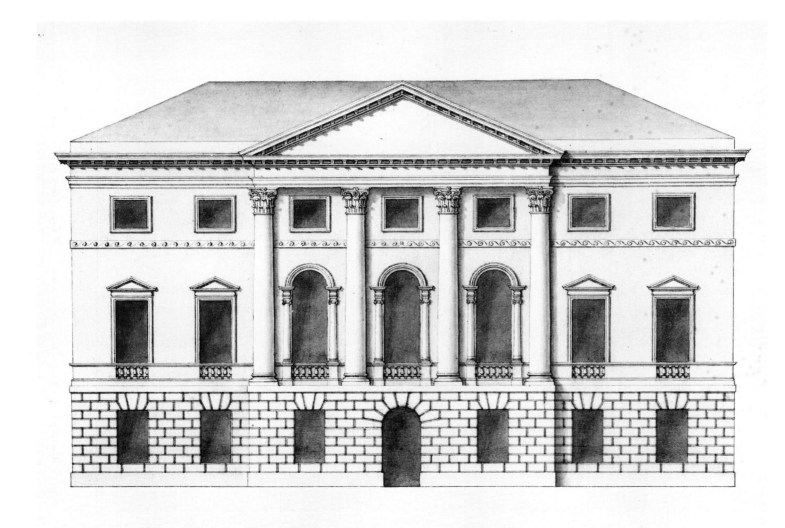

Nathaniel Curzon, as he then was, had engaged Matthew Brettingham in the planning and early stages of rebuilding Kedleston prior to his father's death (November 1758), though meeting Adam in the following month he said he regretted it. Brettingham was responsible for staking the outlines of the plan on site with quadrant colonnades, following the general outline of Palladio's Villa Mocenigo, a favourite source for many of Lord Burlington's followers – like Colen Campbell at Houghton, the mysterious Colonel Moyser, said to have designed Nostell Priory, and the Earl of Leicester, who with Brettingham himself developed the plan of Holkham. Like Lord Leicester, Nathaniel Curzon probably played a major role in the genesis of Kedleston, and it was he who suggested the plan to avoid re-siting the medieval church. Brettingham was responsible for the structure (though not the interior) of the family pavilion on the north-east. After this he was replaced, by James Paine and then by Robert Adam.

This elevation, typical of his static Palladian style, is of seven bays and in the Corinthian order, compared with the executed version in five bays, with the Ionic order, and with straight-topped windows on the first floor instead of arched or pedimented surrounds. The Vitruvian scroll below the attic storey was also omitted. Similar drawings, initialled by Brettingham, can be found at Holkham.

5
Design for an Octagonal Saloon c.1759
attributed to James Paine
pen and ink and wash
$15\frac{1}{4} \times 13\frac{1}{4}$

This drawing, almost certainly in Paine's
hand, is his only known interior design for
Kedleston, and compares with the tribunes
at each end of the sculpture gallery at
Holkham. The idea of a high domed saloon,
arranged with sculpture in niches, is of
particular interest as a possible alternative
to the circular saloon conceived by Lord
Scarsdale, and carried out by Robert
Adam (see no.43).

6
Designs for the North Front c.1759
attributed to James Paine
pen, ink and wash (with two flaps)
$9\frac{3}{4} \times 15\frac{1}{4}$

In Adam's conversation with Curzon in December 1758 there had been no reference to James Paine, though it is possible that he was engaged to execute Matthew Brettingham's designs soon afterwards. The first reference to Paine in the accounts occurs in January 1760 for building the kitchen pavilion and in his later *Plans, Elevations & Sections . . .*, Paine says that he accepted Brettingham's previous design for the "four pavilions or wings" but himself planned "the central block and connecting corridors". His position as Lord Scarsdale's architect for the main block had been terminated by April 1760 however, when Adam was put in sole charge of it. As in Brettingham's case Paine was responsible for the structure, but not the interior, of the kitchen pavilion.

The drawing is for a central *corps de logis* with flanking pavilions attached by quadrants; there are two flaps, so providing three alternatives for the central block. Two of these designs include an attached Corinthian portico of three bays with coupled columns at each end, similar to Paine's west front at Wardour Castle in Wiltshire; each is devoid of direct access to the principal floor. The third design is for a free-standing Ionic hexastyle portico, with more widely spaced columns and external staircases; it is similar to Paine's later engraving published in the second volume of his *Plans, Elevations and Sections . . .* in 1783.

According to Algernon Graves, Paine exhibited a group of designs for an anonymous patron (but evidently for Kedleston) at the Society of Arts in 1761. However these drawings, made in 1759, consisted only of a plan, a garden or south front elevation, and a section.

7
Design for the North Front 1760
Robert Adam
pen, ink and wash
signed and dated
$11\frac{1}{4} \times 46\frac{1}{2}$

Adam had probably produced one copy of
this design by the summer of 1760, by
which time he was in charge of the main
block (and in practice of the quadrants).
That copy (Soane Museum 40:1) was
headed "for Sir Nathaniel Curzon", and
must therefore be prior to April 1761 when
he was raised to the peerage. However the
exhibited drawing is headed "for Lord
Scarsdale" and must have been supplied a
little later (see note on dating, p.14). They
are otherwise almost identical.

The design is similar to the 1783 Paine
engraving. The most important changes
were to reduce the portico from two to one
column in depth and to light the hall from
above, thus dispensing with the windows
under the portico. It was then possible to
substitute niches with sculpture and
medallions above them. The windows on
the pavilion ends of the quadrants were
considerably enlarged, no doubt following
Lord Scarsdale's instructions.

The engraving of the north front in
Woolfe and Gandon's *Vitruvius
Britannicus*, vol.IV, 1767 (plate 47–8),
very closely follows this drawing, though
showing panels in the upper section of the
portico, instead of the medallions and
swags later substituted.

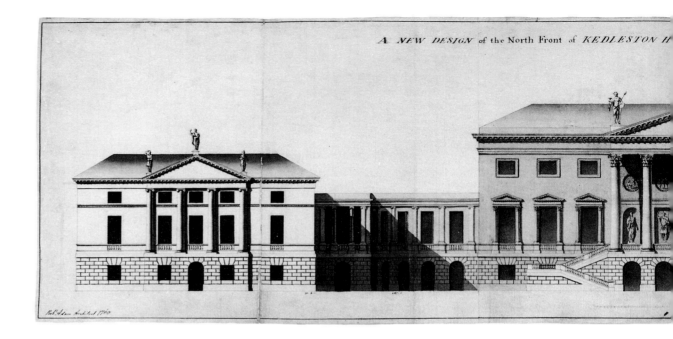

A NEW DESIGN of the North Front of KEDLESTON H

A NEW DESIGN of the SOUTH FRONT of KEDLESTON

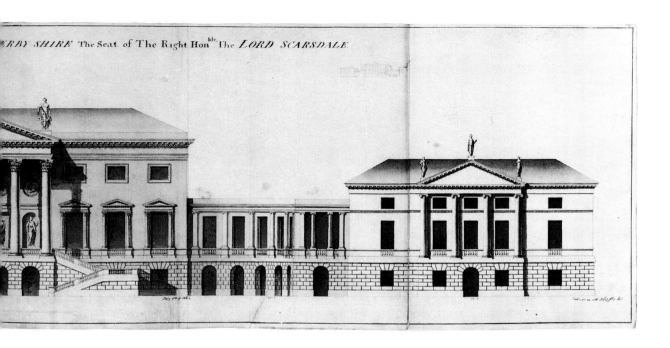

ERBY SHIRE The Seat of The Right Honble The *LORD SCARSDALE*.

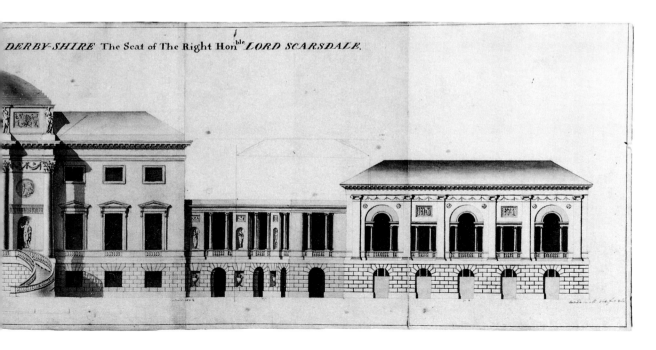

DERBY-SHIRE The Seat of The Right Honble *LORD SCARSDALE*.

8

Design for the South Front 1760
Robert Adam
pen, ink and wash
signed and dated
$11\frac{1}{4} \times 46\frac{3}{4}$

The relationship between this drawing and
the version in the Soane Museum (40:2) is
the same as for the north front (no.7).

The concept of the projecting rotunda,
as published by Paine in 1783, was almost
certainly due to Lord Scarsdale himself (to
be fully discussed in my forthcoming book
on Kedleston). Robert Adam's design
retained the rotunda inside as the Saloon,
but applied the Arch of Constantine
outside; an arrangement which was
undoubtedly his own contribution. By
placing the Arch in front of the rotunda
with its five-stepped dome, Adam drew a
parallel with the six-stepped dome of the
Pantheon and its octastyle temple front.
At the same time the way in which the
columns and their entablatures break out
from the façade, combined with the curves
of the dome and staircase, give a feeling of
movement, or in his own words (from the
Works in Architecture of 1773) "the rise and
fall, the advance and recess with other
diversity of form, in the different parts of a
building, so as to add greatly to the
picturesque of the composition". Sadly the
quadrants and pavilions, which were so
important a part of his scheme, had been
abandoned by the autumn of 1764. In 1768
he provided another design for completing
the front, but this was not achieved either
(see no.10).

During a restoration in recent times
resources did not allow the steps of the
dome to be replaced but the method
adopted will allow this to be done in the
future; old photographs show them in
place.

The engraving in *Vitruvius Britannicus*
(vol.IV, 1767, plate 49–50) is almost
identical to the drawing, except for the
omission of the statues, urns and bas-reliefs
on the quadrants and wings.

9
Plan of the Principal Floor c.1764–65
(with a flap added c.1768)
Robert Adam
pen, ink and wash, with inscriptions in
sepia ink and pencil
$11\frac{1}{2} \times 19\frac{1}{4}$

In broad terms there are three sets of plans of Kedleston. The earliest, among the Adam drawings in the Soane Museum (40:5,6,7), show the basement, principal and attic floors, and each measure about $47'' \times 34''$. They are of c.1760, with Adam's great dressing room (nos.33–34) at the centre of the west front, and the great stair (no.35) rising only to the principal floor.

The second group consists of two smaller plans, still at Kedleston: one of the principal floor (that under discussion) and one of the attic floor. These show the post–1764 arrangement of the principal apartment, without the great dressing room, and with the great stair rising to the attic floor. There is also a basement plan of about the same size as those in the Soane Museum, but so delicate that it cannot at present be examined, and it is unclear to which group it belongs. The third and final group of plans are those in Woolfe & Gandon's *Vitruvius Britannicus*, vol.IV, 1767 (plates 45,46) showing the basement and principal floors (the latter very closely following the Kedleston drawing), but no attic.

Without the southern quadrants and pavilions which are pasted on to the Kedleston drawing, the plan of the principal floor is an accurate record of the situation reached by 1768, and which continued undisturbed until after the death of the 4th Lord Scarsdale in 1916. Since then there have been a few minor changes, but nothing affecting the state rooms which could not easily be rectified.

With the abandonment of the southern pavilions, more thought was given to completing the south front, and in 1768 Adam suggested attaching square pavilions at each end of the main block (no.10). The Painted Breakfasting Room (nos.41–42) would have been at the west end and the Book Room (no.40) at the east. No doubt problems of cost did not permit the achievement of these proposals.

The pencil inscription at top left, probably in Lord Scarsdale's hand, reads "Between the End Room & the Library should be folding Doors very Large or a Screen of Columns that the View of the very broad part of the River may be taken from the Salloon Door or farther" – showing the importance which he attached to the views of the landscape seen from the house.

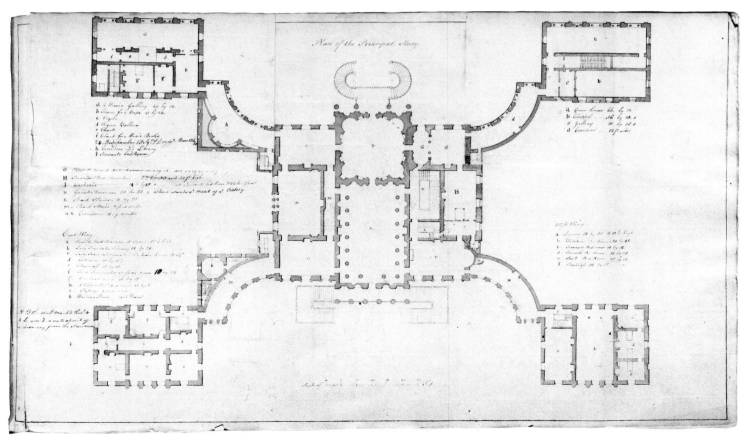

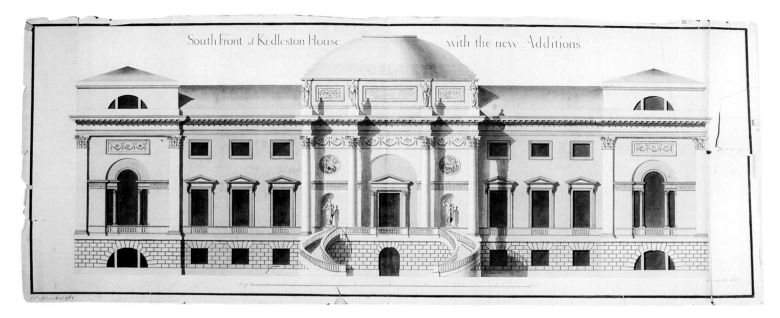

South Front of Kedleston House with the new Additions.

10
Design for the South Front
1768
Robert Adam
pen, ink and wash
20 × 50

This revised elevation for the south front was made following the abandonment of the quadrants and southern pavilions (seen in no.8) about 1765. In their place, Adam now suggested smaller square "pavilions" with shallow pyramid roofs, joined to the ends of the main block. These were to contain (on the principal floor) a "Book Room" at the east end (no.40), and a "Painted Breakfasting Room" at the west end (nos.41–42). The therm window below the latter would have perfectly suited the grotto scheme initially devised by Adam for the "Rock Room" in the garden at Ireton (see no.70). The scheme was never to be executed, and in some ways the south front is more dramatic as a result.

Detail of No. 9, with the flap lowered to show Adam's revised scheme of 1768

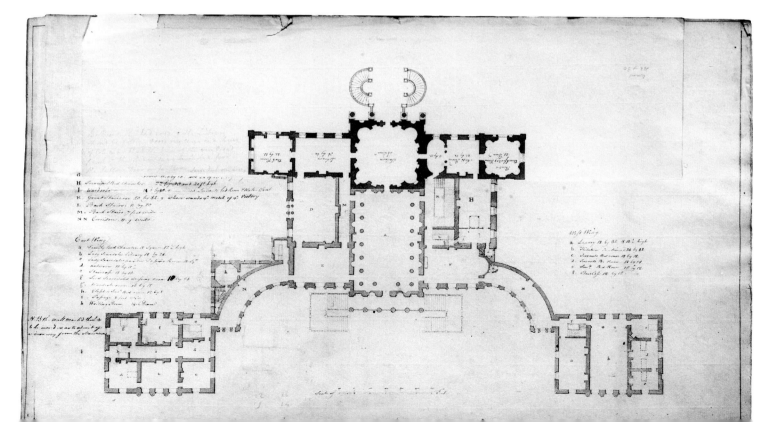

11–14
Four designs for decorating a State Room c.1757–58
James "Athenian" Stuart
pen, ink and watercolour
chimneypiece wall: $15 \times 21\frac{3}{4}$;
end wall with sideboard: $15 \times 12\frac{3}{4}$;
end wall with "tempietto": $14 \times 12\frac{3}{4}$;
window wall: $13\frac{3}{4} \times 20\frac{1}{2}$.

These four drawings appear initially to be for the same room, which was to be 50 by 30 feet. Closer examination leads to some doubt as to their mutual suitability, although there are matching features.

The window wall with an external entrance, would be suitable for a hall or a saloon. If the latter it would fit appropriately with the chimneypiece wall, in the corner of which a copy of the Venus de Medici stands on a pedestal, matching the Bacchus, Ceres, and other statues on the opposite side. The chimneypiece, with its lion masks is almost identical to one at Nuneham Park, Oxfordshire, designed by Stuart about 1760, but has wreaths inspired by those on the Choragic Monument of Thrasyllus.

The pairs of tripods on the chimneypiece and the pier tables are of the same form as an ormolu perfume-burner (supposedly derived from the tripod which crowned the Choragic Monument of Lysicrates in Athens), which still survives in the house. Although it appears in the centre of Adam's sideboard arrangement for the dining room (no.15), both Lord Scarsdale and his son describe it as being designed by Stuart – as does the Duchess of Northumberland, visiting Kedleston in 1766 (see no.16). Similar tripods (presumably in plasterwork) can be seen above the four doors, and other variants, designed by Stuart for Wentworth Woodhouse in Yorkshire, and for Spencer House in London, were probably made by Diederich Nicolaus Anderson, whose signature appears on the plate-warmer at Kedleston (see no.18).

One of the drawings for the end walls shows the marble wine-cooler, also designed by Stuart and supplied by Richard Hayward the sculptor (together with the cast of Mercury on the left of the window wall) in January 1758. The pedestals in the recess support the two large silver wine-fountains, once again to appear in Adam's dining room niche (see no.16). The full-length portrait of Nathaniel Curzon and his wife is a fascinating precursor of that painted by Nathaniel Hone in 1761 (illustrated on p.9).

The drawing for the other end wall shows at the upper level the two large pictures by Benedetto Luti, bought by Curzon in London in February 1757, and with a painting of his own composition, based on the frieze of the Choragic Monument of Lysicrates, above the central arched recess.

Within the recess itself there is a remarkable temple-like structure, with a large urn on a pedestal in front of it. Preparation was being made for a large Snetzler organ to be temporarily accommodated in Curzon's London house in June 1758. Presumably it must have been ordered some time before this, and it is just possible that Stuart's drawing represents an organ case, though where the organist was to sit remains a mystery.

The relationship of the long walls to the end walls would have caused a problem as they are shown, for the statues on pedestals in the corners would have impeded the doorways. Stuart's designs may indeed not have been for a "real" room in a properly planned house – and perhaps he even intended them to be adapted for use as a saloon, a dining room or a music room to taste, since all these rooms would be needed. However it was the decorative scheme as a whole, with its advanced neo-classical vocabulary, that mattered – and that must have been intended to appeal to Nathaniel Curzon's scholarly tastes, before Robert Adam's arrival on the scene.

Curzon's reaction to these proposals can hardly have been favourable, to judge by Adam's letter to his brother James in December 1758 (Clerk of Penicuik mss. 4854), where he describes how "... Sir Nathaniel brought me out a Design of the Great Athenians for his Rooms finishing ... so excessively & so ridiculously bad, that [he] immediately saw the folly of them & said so to some people which so offended the proud Grecian, that he has not seen Sr. Nathaniel these 2 years [evidently an exaggeration] ...". Adam goes on to describe one particular design, including "... Tables of 2 foot sqr. in a Room of 50 foot long with belts of Stone & great pannels of Roses & festoon & figures all Ramm'd in wherever there was a hole to be got for them", almost certainly referring to the elevation of the window wall in this group (no.14).

According to Adam, Stuart also "wanted to fitt frames for Sir Nathaniel's pictures but not having or rather I suppose, not being willing to confine his great genius to the sizes of the pictures, he cuts 3 foot off the length of the best pictures and 2 foot off the height of others to make them answer and draws all the pictures and colours them in his drawings. But they move pity rather than contempt". Despite these strictures, Adam's own designs for the dining room at Kedleston (nos.15–16) took a leaf out of Stuart's book, not only in details like the sideboard niche, but also in the general presentation of his highly finished coloured drawings.

Literature: Watkin, 32–34, figs.20–23; Goodison, 695–703, figs.62,69–71

15
Design for the West End of the Dining Room 1762
Robert Adam
pen, ink and watercolour, with pencil additions
signed and dated
$13\frac{1}{2} \times 17\frac{3}{4}$

Horace Walpole, recording his visit to the house in 1768, noted "The Great Parlour in the best taste of all". Adam provided elevations of each wall with pictures set out in their final (and present) positions; although dated 1762 they were probably produced a few years later. The niche wall appears in an uncoloured version, but also in this outstanding coloured drawing complete with sideboards, pedestals and buffet arrangement – perhaps executed with special care to rival Stuart's earlier design for a similar sideboard niche.

In execution the radiating design of the semi-dome was up-ended and it centred from above. A broad anthemion frieze was added at its base and carried across the full width of this end of the room. This frieze was included in the office copies (Soane Museum 40:20–23), but not in those at Kedleston. It unfortunately clashes (on the left) with the pediment of the adjacent door, suggesting a change not properly assimilated with the earlier scheme.

The elaborate colour scheme, with lavish use of gilding for the doorcases, picture frames and entablature may never have been executed as Adam suggested, for the Duchess of Northumberland recorded in 1766 that "the Sideboard stands in an Alcove the stucco ornaments of which are white upon a green Ground". Scientific analysis of the paintwork in the room has yet to be carried out. The overdoor paintings of mythological subjects, described as "Sacrifices to Hygeia" in the 1769 and 1771 Kedleston catalogues, were to be replaced by William Collins' stucco roundels of the Harvest and Vintage (see nos.19–20).

Design of the West End of the Dining Room with the Niche & Sideboard

Robᵗ Adam Architect 1762.

16
Design for the Sideboard Niche in the Dining Room 1762
Robert Adam
pen, ink and wash
signed and dated
$17\frac{3}{4} \times 23\frac{3}{4}$ (cut down to fit bound volume)

This drawing is an enlargement of the alcove, as shown in the coloured drawing of the dining room (no.15); a plan of the niche also survives at Kedleston. The three carved tables and two pairs of pedestals were made by the carpenters and carvers for £21.2.0, and are among the earliest of Adam's neo-classical furniture designs, although preceded by the scagliola-topped tables, with frames also carved at Kedleston, now in the family corridor.

The gilt-bronze tripod, two chestnut vases and four of the knife boxes all remain in the house. The tripod was designed by Athenian Stuart, and perhaps also the vases, and possibly made by Diederich Nicolaus Anderson (see no.18). They were at once provided with small pedestals by the carvers, and the pedestals for the fountains and cisterns were also heightened.

The two silver wine-fountains and two cisterns were unfortunately sold in 1947, the latter now belonging to the Victoria and Albert Museum and the Goldsmiths' Company respectively. One fountain (an extremely rare example of French silver of the 1660s, with the handles added in England at a later date) was recently acquired by the J. Paul Getty Museum, but the location of the other (made to match by the English smith, Ralph Leeke in the 1690s) is unknown (Wilson, 1–12).

The Duchess of Northumberland writing about the alcove noted that "it is adorn'd with a vast quantity of handsome plate judiciously dispos'd on Tables of beautiful Marble & of very pretty shapes in the midst is Mr Stewarts Tripod the cut Decanters are all bound with Silver wch has a mighty pretty effect". There are no known photographs showing the ensemble with all its components, but it is hoped in time to make copies of the fountains and cisterns, and thus recreate one of the most important features of the house.

Literature: E. Harris, fig.3; Wilson, fig.13

Drawing at Large of the Side Board in the Nich of the Dining Room at Kedleston

Robt Adam Architect 1762

Design of the Ceiling of the Dining Room

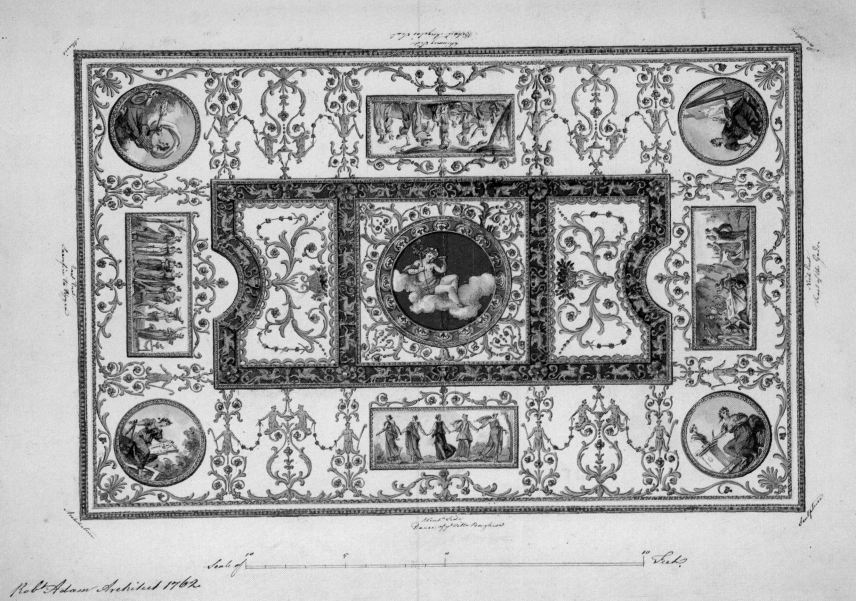

Scale of   5   Feet

Rob.t Adam Architect 1762.

The west end of the Dining Room, showing
the sideboard niche

17

Design for the Ceiling of the Dining Room
1762
Robert Adam
pen, ink and watercolour
signed and dated
$14\frac{1}{2} \times 19\frac{1}{2}$

The colours are principally yellow and
blue, although it has often been suggested
that the yellow was intended to represent
gilding. In the accounts only the picture
frames are actually recorded as being gilt.
The Duchess of Northumberland recorded
in 1766 that "the Ceiling is on a Pale
Purple Ground & very pretty", which
again makes it doubtful whether the colour
scheme shown in the drawing was ever
executed.

The source of the design appears to be
the same as for one of the engravings of the
so-called "Palace of Augustus" in the
Farnese Gardens (plate 54) from Charles
Cameron's *Baths of the Romans*, published
in 1772.

The subjects of the ceiling paintings are
given in Adam's inscriptions on the
drawing: in the roundels at the four
corners, personifications of Sculpture,
Painting, Music and Architecture; and in
the rectangular panels "Windo Side/Dance
of ye Villa Borghese", "Nich End/Feast of
the Gods", "Chimney side/Michael
Angelo's Seal", and "East End/Sacrifice to
Hygea". The youthful Bacchus shown in
the centre is appropriate as the presiding
genius of the dining room, with thyrsus,
cup and garland of vine leaves.

All these paintings were carried out and
installed in 1768: scaffolding was put up
for the purpose in June, but in October
Adam reported seeing another set of
paintings for Kedleston at Zucchi's studio
"almost completed". The 1769 catalogue
describes them – the only difference from
Adam's drawing being the substitution of
"Poetry" for "Sculpture" – but Lord
Scarsdale evidently had second thoughts,
for Bray in 1777 lists a wholly different
scheme, as exists today: the *Four
Continents* in the corners, by Zucchi; the
Four Seasons in the oblong panels, by

William Hamilton; and *Love Embracing
Fortune* in the centre, by Henry Robert
Morland. However the c.1796 Kedleston
catalogue gives all the paintings to Zucchi,
so some doubt as to their authorship
remains.

Although Adam must take the credit for
this, and the other sheets in the collection
which bear his signature, most of them
must have been carried out by draughtsmen in his office. The highly accomplished
figures in this drawing (like those for the
Painted Breakfast Room in the family
pavilion – see nos.37–39) suggest the hand
of the Italian artist, Agostino Brunias,
who was employed by Adam in Rome, and
accompanied him back to England in 1757.

Plate-Warmer
now in Dining Room

18
Design for a Plate Warmer c.1757
attributed to James "Athenian" Stuart
pen, ink and wash
$14\frac{1}{4} \times 8\frac{1}{4}$

The outline of the urn has been cut out
from its original sheet and pasted on to the
page. There is a more accurate drawing in
the Soane Museum (25:15) inscribed "for
Sir Nathaniel Curzon Bart" and thus
dating from before 1761; however this
appears to be merely a record drawing
taken from the piece itself (as with other
drawings of the silver at Kedleston now in
the Soane collection). The differences
between the Kedleston drawing and the
plate-warmer as executed, suggest by
contrast that this was the original proposal
from which the design was developed.

The maker is not in doubt; he recorded
his name and date on the concealed rim
"Diederich Nicolaus Anderson made this
Plate-Warmer in the year 1760". The
designer is not known, but Stuart seems a
distinct possibility, particularly as
Anderson displayed "a tripod, from an
original design of Mr Stuart's" at the Free
Society of Artists in 1761 (Gunnis, 17). In
the early Kedleston catalogues, the plate
warmer was described as "Copper gilt after
an Antique Bas relievo". It is $34\frac{1}{2}$ inches
high including an added pedestal made by
the carpenters and carvers, and may once
have contained a small burner to heat the
plates, compensating for the fact that the
kitchen at Kedleston was in a separate
wing, some way away from the dining
room. The Duchess of Northumberland
described it in 1766 as being "in the shape
of a vase and extremely handsome".

(Right) The plate-warmer, as executed

19–20
Designs for the Medallions of "Vintage" and "Harvest" in the Dining Room c.1771–78
attributed to William Collins
pen, ink and wash
$9\frac{1}{4} \times 7\frac{1}{2}$

Originally there were circular paintings
above the doors on the west wall of the
dining room, as shown in Adam's drawing
(see no.15), but some time between the
1771 and 1778 Kedleston catalogues, they
were replaced by plaster reliefs by William
Collins (1721–1793), a pupil of Sir Henry
Cheere, who also carved the five stone
medallions under the portico of the north
front in 1769. These drawings were
recently discovered at Kedleston, and are
assumed to be in his hand. There were a
number of changes from the drawings in
execution, particularly in the "Harvest".

An identical plaster relief of the
"Vintage" now hangs in the vestibule of
the Sir John Soane Museum.

(organ not executed)

Robt Adam Architect 1763.

21
Design for the West Wall of the Music Room 1760
Robert Adam
pen, ink and wash
signed and dated
$14\frac{1}{4} \times 20\frac{3}{4}$

This drawing is one of a set of elevations of all four walls of the Music Room together with a ceiling design, signed and dated as above, but probably drawn c.1765 (see note on p.14). The large organ (to be enclosed in the splendid case on the west wall) was supplied and installed by John Snetzler in Curzon's London house in 1758, but it is improbable that it ever reached Kedleston.

Before the abandonment of the southern pavilions, there had been a proposal to install the instrument in the "musick gallery" in the south east pavilion. In the event it was sold back to Snetzler, and a smaller organ requiring a less bulky case was substituted for it.

22
Design for an Organ 1762
Robert Adam
pen, ink and wash (and inscribed in pencil "Si placeo, tuum est")
signed and dated
$20\frac{1}{4} \times 13\frac{1}{2}$

The organ case shown in this drawing was only about 11 feet 6 inches high, compared with 18 feet in the previous drawing, and the instrument seems to have been "an old one", according to one of Samuel Wyatt's letters to Lord Scarsdale written about this time. The case executed by the carpenters and carvers was a simplified version of the drawing, but it retained the overall shape and the Ionic order which was the architectural motif of the Music Room. There is also a drawing of the organ case in profile in the collection. Since the re-attribution of the organ case at Newby in Yorkshire to Athenian Stuart (Watkin, 41), that at Kedleston may be Adam's only surviving organ – though there are equally elaborate designs for instruments at Home House in Portman Square and Sir Watkin Williams-Wynn's house in St. James Square, the latter with very similar caryatids supporting the pipes (Soane Museum 40:71).

23
Design for a Painted Ceiling 1758
Michael Henry Spang
watercolour
signed and dated
$12\frac{1}{4} \times 19\frac{1}{4}$

The sculptor, Michael Henry Spang, arrived in England from Denmark about 1756, and was paid £28 by Nathaniel Curzon in August 1758 for carving four figures in wood, which still survive in the Caesars' Hall (below the Marble Hall) at Kedleston. Other payments are recorded to him about this time, before Curzon succeeded his father, and before his first meeting with Adam in December – and Spang received a total of £990 for carving marble chimneypieces in three of the principal rooms in 1759–61.

From the scale it can be estimated that the ceiling depicted here would have measured 47 by 28 feet. Presumably intended for Kedleston, it would (at this date) have related to a room designed by Stuart or Paine. If the Paine plan had followed that by Brettingham then only the equivalent of the present drawing room, then 44 by 30 feet, could have been in any way relevant.

The style is decidedly Rococo as one might expect and the subjects relate to the maritime aspects of the Seven Years War, then at its height – although it was not until the following year, 1759 (the so-called "Year of Victories") that French invasion plans were finally thwarted by Admiral Hawke's success at Quiberon Bay. In the centre Britannia is supported by Neptune and Mars, while Hawke may well be one of the admirals depicted in medallions on charts of their battles, or held by putti in the border, together with Boscawen, Anson and Vernon – although the Van Dyck dress of some of the others suggest earlier heroes of the 17th-century Dutch Wars, like Admiral Blake. Nathaniel Curzon's particular interest in naval matters can also be judged from two large, fully rigged models of men-of-war which survive in their original glazed cases at Kedleston (one of them supplied through Spang's agency in January, 1759; and the other made by French prisoners-of-war in Derby), and indeed it is very likely that Scarsdale dictated the form and iconography of Spang's surprisingly assured design. If the watercolour was indeed made with the drawing room in mind, it might explain the nautical theme still to be found in the sea-monsters of Adam's plasterwork ceiling (no.24).

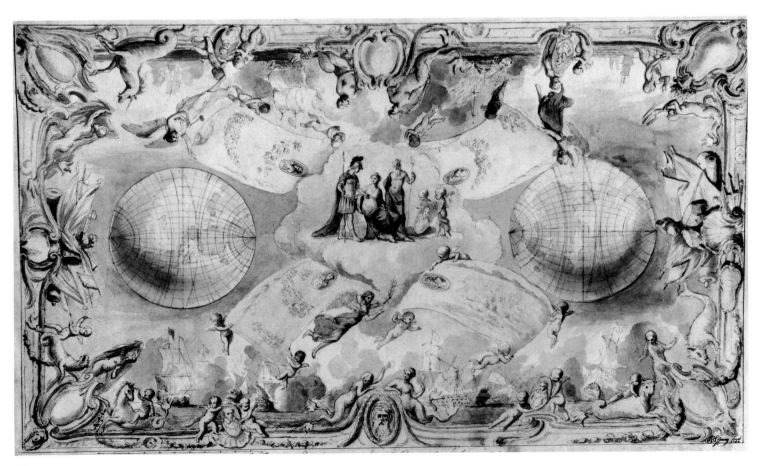

24
Design for the Drawing Room Ceiling 1759
Robert Adam
pen, ink and watercolour
signed and dated
17 × 23

This coloured drawing belongs with a set of
four (uncoloured) wall elevations for the
drawing room, all signed and dated 1760,
but again probably produced c.1765 (see
note on p.14). However, it is not
improbable that the design existed in 1759,
and indeed there are parallels in Adam's
designs made for Admiral Boscawen at
Hatchlands at this date. The first firm date
we have for it is November 1760, when
Adam reported that he had sent his copy of
the ceiling to the plasterer, Joseph Rose,
for costing.

In his preface "Of Ceilings and Wall
Decorations" in the *Works in Architecture*,
Adam makes clear his disapproval of large
fresco compositions on ceilings, which he
thought tired the patience of any
spectator, and preferred instead
"grotesque" ornaments and figures which
could be appreciated without neck-
straining effort. In this instance, the
looseness of the acanthus scrolls and the
boldness of the design as a whole are
typical of his early (still in some respects
Rococo-influenced) style, developed in the
years after his return from Rome. The
caryatid figures echo those of Spang's
marble chimneypiece, and the sea-
monsters pick up the naval theme of
Linnell's sofas (see no.27) thus giving the
room a decorative unity. The present pale
pink and blue colour scheme, following the
original, was carried out for Lord Curzon in
the early years of this century.

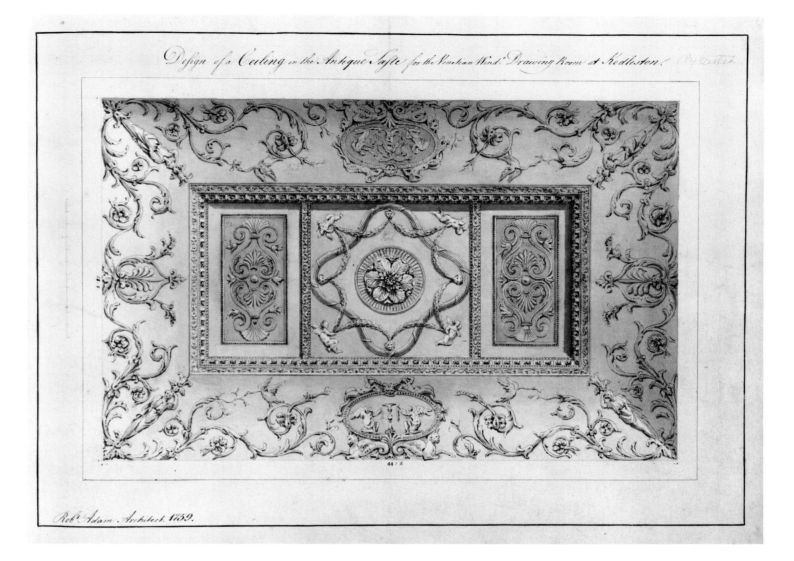

25
Design for a Girandole for the Drawing Room 1767
Robert Adam
pen and ink and watercolour
signed and dated
$17 \times 11\frac{1}{2}$

A pair of very similar oval gilt-framed pier glasses were designed by Adam for the Drawing Room in 1765 (Soane Museum 20:8) and executed by the carvers at Kedleston by the end of that year.

This design of 1767 was for a pair of matching (but rather thinner) girandoles to be placed either side of the chimneypiece on the opposite wall between the pictures. However they are not mentioned in the early catalogues or inventories, and seem never to have been made.

26
Design for a Candlestand for the Drawing Room late 1750s
anon
pen, ink and wash
$11\frac{1}{4} \times 7\frac{1}{2}$

A pair of Rococo torchères made almost exactly to this design stood in the Drawing Room until 1930, when they were sold to meet death duties. It is assumed that they would originally have stood in the inner corners of the room.

In the later 1750s, before inheriting Kedleston, Nathaniel Curzon was not only buying pictures for the house, but also furniture from various cabinet makers, inevitably in the Rococo taste; these included the carvers and gilders, Samuel Norman and James Whittle, who supplied candlestands of rather similar form for Petworth House in Sussex early in the following decade.

William Linnell, who delivered a large amount of furniture for the Curzon's London house in Audley Square in 1758, would be another possible candidate, particularly as his son and partner John Linnell was adept at producing designs of this sort (see no.27).

The torchères are now the only elements missing from the room as it was furnished in the 18th century, and it is to be hoped that replicas of them will be made in due course.

Literature: Coleridge, fig.289 (showing the candlestands as executed)

Sketch design for a Sofa c.1762
attributed to John Linnell
pen, ink and wash
$6 \times 9\frac{1}{4}$

The four sofas made for the Drawing Room at Kedleston by John Linnell are among the very grandest pieces of seat furniture ever made in Britain. In 1762, Adam had produced a design of a sofa for Lord Scarsdale (Soane Museum 17:69) with some of the same features, including caryatid supports. But these designs were radically altered in execution by the carver John Linnell, perhaps at Lord Scarsdale's instigation, and it may be for this reason that Adam then offered his design to another client, Mrs. Montagu, for her house in Portman Square.

Horace Walpole described the Kedleston sofas in 1768 (three years after their arrival at the house) as "settees supported by gilt fishes and sea gods absurdly like the King's coach" (Toynbee, 64). George III's famous coronation coach, attributed to Sir William Chambers, was carved by Joseph Wilton in 1760, but at the same time Linnell had produced a rival proposal for it, also decorated with mermaid and triton caryatids; significantly, he dedicated his engraving to Lord Scarsdale (Hayward and Kirkham, fig.148)

The Linnells, at first William (d.1763), and then his son John (1729–96), gave regular service to Lord Scarsdale's London houses at least from August 1758 until 1796. It would not be difficult to visualize the younger Linnell, who was a talented draughtsman, producing this sketch on one of these occasions; there is no record that he ever actually visited Kedleston, but he provided important furniture for the house on later occasions, including a pair of marquetry card tables made for the Drawing Room, where they still remain.

The sofas can be seen in the illustration of the Drawing Room on p.10.

Five designs for the Library 1760
Robert Adam
pen, ink and wash
signed and dated
ceiling: $14\frac{1}{4} \times 19$; wall elevations $14\frac{1}{4} \times 20\frac{1}{4}$

As with the preceding Music Room and Drawing Room, Adam provided finished drawings for all four walls and the ceiling of the Library, shown here as a group. The drawings were probably produced about 1765, despite the fact that they bear an earlier date – which is likely to be that of their first conception (see below; and note on p.14).

The design of the "Mosaic Ceiling" has recurring motifs which could be extended in either direction without limit, as in the kind of antique Roman mosaic pavements Adam had seen in Italy, both in Rome and in Ravenna. It would be suitable for a gallery, and is in fact strikingly similar to Adam's executed design (Soane Museum 11:36) for the gallery at Croome Court in Worcestershire. The fact that the Kedleston drawing is in *grisaille* implies that (like the Music Room) the Library ceiling was never intended to be picked out in different colours.

With the numerous architectural interruptions caused by doors, windows and chimneypiece, a number of separated bookcases was inevitable, and those on each wall are of different sizes. Above the cornices they were originally provided with swan neck pediments, and pedestals for busts. These were probably removed about 1830 and do not survive, but sufficient evidence is available for satisfactory restoration. At the same time the doors of the bookcases, executed with glazing bars which echo the octagons of the ceiling, were also removed, but these were fortunately stored, and have recently been replaced.

For some time the long bookcase shown on the east wall posed a problem, for a door (or doors here) would have been essential for access to the south east quadrant and pavilion. There are drawings at Kedleston and the Soane Museum (40:11) showing this arrangement, and indeed false doors were actually made for this wall, flanking a smaller bookcase. The explanation must be that the drawings, although dated 1760, were produced after the abandonment of the southern pavilions, about 1765, but inscribed with the date the decoration was first conceived. The fact that the pictures shown on this wall are un-named (in contrast with the other walls) helps to support this argument.

In Adam's other country house libraries there were generally fewer doorways, and he was able to provide bookcases continuously along some walls. However, at Kedleston it was obviously too late to make this adjustment. The doors were removed about 1830 to provide more book space, and re-used in 1923 on the great staircase, but it is hoped that they will eventually be returned to their original positions.

The drawing for the window wall shows the two smallest bookcases, on the piers. The festoon curtains leave the moulded window frames attractively clear of drapery, and allow unimpeded views over the park to the south.

The west wall is dominated by the large Doric door case, an appropriate entrance to the lofty Saloon beyond. Its frieze is decorated with three varieties of metope, like those in the frieze immediately below the cornice. The Doric order (also followed by the chimneypiece) may well have been Lord Scarsdale's choice, thus completing the classical trio of Ionic and Corinthian in the previous two rooms. Comparable libraries by Adam at Croome, Osterley and Nostell Priory were all of the Ionic order.

The final picture arrangement in the Library is indicated in the drawings, all except for the "Chiaro oscuro" over the door to the Saloon (a space that remained empty until the 1790s), and the un-named picture immediately above the chimneypiece, where the much larger Rembrandt School *Daniel Interpreting the Dream of Nebuchadnezzar* now hangs.

Mosaic Ceiling for The Library — (Executed.)

Robt Adam Architect. 1760.

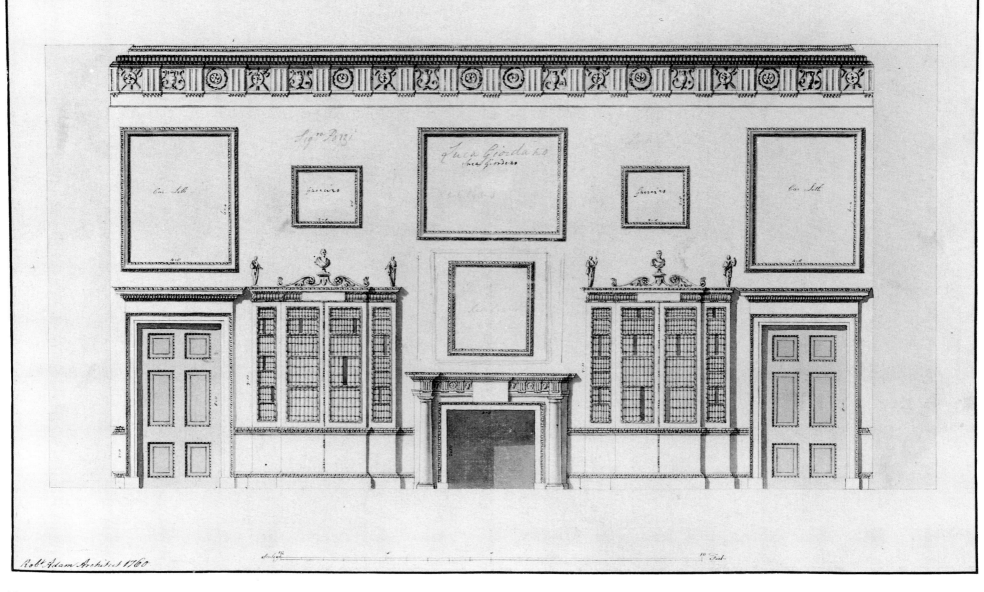

Rob.t Adam Architect 1760

Section of the East End of the Library

Rob.t Adam Architect 1760.

Rob.t Adam Architect 1760.

Scale

Feet

46

Rob.t Adam Architect 1760.

Chimney Side of the Great Dressing Room for Kedleston House   (not executed)

Scale of   5   Feet

Rob.t Adam Architect 1762.

33

Design for the State Dressing Room
1762
Robert Adam
pen, ink and wash
signed and dated
$14\frac{1}{2} \times 19$

The original intention in the first Adam plan (Soane Museum 40:6) had been to place an apse-ended state dressing room at the centre of the west front where the present state bedchamber is (balancing the drawing room on the east). It would have been reduced in height to avoid squeezing the semi-state rooms above. However when the southern pavilions were abandoned Lord Scarsdale changed the plan of the principal apartment to the present arrangement of ante-chamber, principal dressing room, state bedchamber, and wardrobe.

This cross-section showing the east wall is one of three drawings for the room. That for the west wall shows an elegant flat-topped Venetian window of the Ionic order, which had been installed before the change of plan required its removal. The apses were not to have received semi-domes (as for instance in the State Dining Room at Syon) and the central rectangle was to have a coved ceiling.

The painting of classical ruins would have had a stucco frame, and classical medallions are shown over the doors. However, in place of the pictures shown by Adam, Lord Scarsdale's pencilled inscriptions at the bottom of the drawing suggest that he was considering hanging the Cuyp (now in the Drawing Room) over the chimneypiece, and portraits over the doors. The chimneypiece bears some resemblance to that in the present bedchamber, but without its central blue-john tablet.

34

Design of a Ceiling for the State Dressing Room 1763
Robert Adam
pen, ink and wash
signed and dated
$14\frac{1}{2} \times 20\frac{1}{2}$

The equivalent partly finished version of this drawing in the Soane Museum (11:52) has an (added) date of 1761. The fluted frieze which appears in the sections (see no.33) was certainly a feature appearing in Adam designs dated 1761 (as at Bowood; Soane Museum 28:52). It also appears in the string above the niches in Adam's design for the Marble Hall at Kedleston, but in the much smaller scale of the dressing room the effect is more emphatic. The continuous garlands shown in the cove are rather different from those proposed in the preceding drawing.

West Side of the Great Staircase for Kedlestone

Scale

Rob.t Adam Architect 1764.

35
**Design for the West Side of the Great
Staircase** 1764
Robert Adam
pen, ink and wash
signed and dated
$20\frac{1}{2} \times 14\frac{1}{2}$

The great staircase suffered a change of
plan during building work. It was
originally intended, as in the drawing, to
reach only to the principal floor, with
access to the "semi-state rooms" on the
floor above provided by the adjacent back
stair. The original stair was already in
place, when it was decided to carry it to the
upper floor with an access landing on the
west side of the stairwell, saving the
necessity for a corridor behind, and thus
making the rooms slightly larger. Fresh
drawings were prepared with changes in
detail to the stucco decorations, but these
were only finally carried out by the
plasterers, Jackson & Co. for Lord Curzon
in 1923–24.

Adam's top-lit rectangular staircase was
not particularly rewarding, and the loss of
the cove did not help. The top landing was
provided with four large paintings
including an early Gavin Hamilton painted
in Rome; however they have suffered an
excess of sun. The lower landings were
enlivened with life-size plaster statues, four
of which – a Bacchus after Sansovino, a
Flora after an ancient statue in the Capitol,
Santa Susanna, and the Priestess of Isis –
still survive.

36
Design for the Ceiling of the Great Staircase
1764
Robert Adam
pen, ink and watercolour
signed and dated
$14\frac{1}{2} \times 20\frac{1}{2}$

In the preceding drawing the ceiling was to
be coved, but due to the insertion of the
upper landing there was insufficient height,
so the cove was omitted and the ceiling
became flat. The carpenters provided a
panelled ceiling as indicated, but the
plasterwork (like that on the walls) was
only carried out in 1923–24.

Adam's watercolour is of particular
interest in showing six alternative colour
schemes, some of them of surprising
intensity.

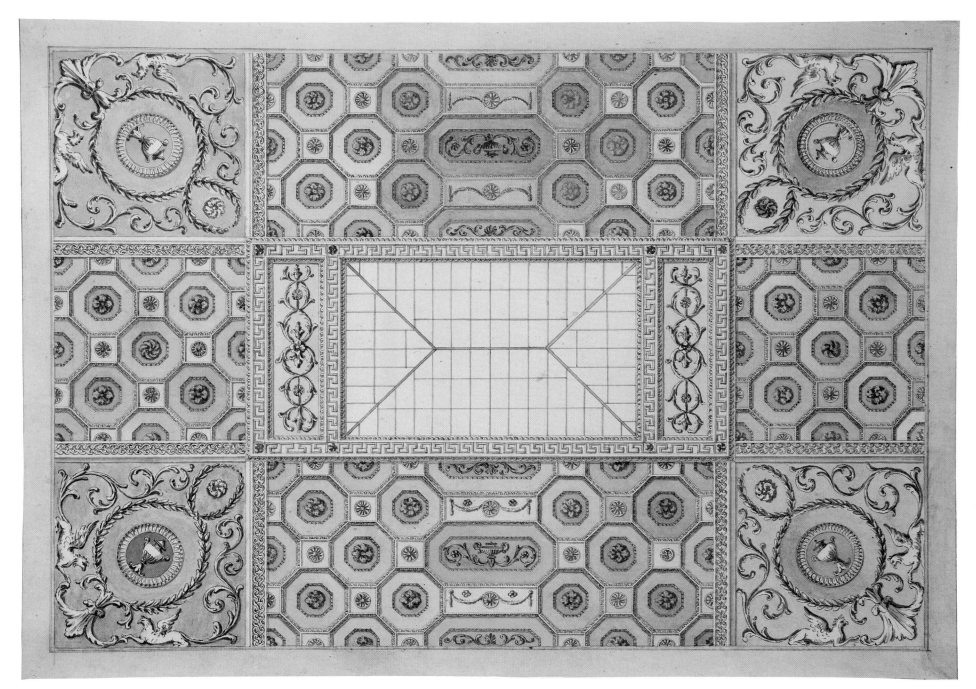

37–39

Three designs for the Painted Breakfast Room in the Family Pavilion 1760

Robert Adam

pen, ink and watercolour

wall elevations $8\frac{1}{2} \times 12$; ceiling $10\frac{3}{4} \times 10\frac{3}{4}$

In July 1760 Robert Adam wrote to his brother James "I have done a painted room for him [i.e. Sir Nathaniel Curzon], which is quite in a new taste & I have Brunias now employed in painting in size to learn that method as oyl colours will by no means answer. They call that manner of painting in French, á la detrempe, and I think he succeeds wonderfully with it." A month later he records that the five drawings (four wall elevations and a ceiling design) were sent up to Kedleston in a small box, and there they have remained, framed and glazed, ever since.

The Painted Breakfast Room (not to be confused with the "Painted Breakfasting Room" planned for the west end of the south front in 1768 – but never executed) began life as "Lady Caroline's Dressing Room", a space only 18 feet square occupying the north-west corner of the family pavilion. Adam's decorative scheme, probably inspired by "Athenian" Stuart's Painted Room at Spencer House, was to be carried out on rolls of paper in London, and, planning a trip to Kedleston in June 1761, he asks Sir Nathaniel "to appoint the people who are to Cut out & Paste up the ornaments that they might be present, so as to put them on the method of doing it right".

The artist was the Italian, Agostino Brunias, who was discovered by Adam in Rome, and brought back to England as one of his chief draughtsmen (see no.17). According to the 1769 catalogue, the room was "finished with fresco paintings and antique ornaments, after the Baths of Dioclesian", and the ceiling design is indeed a close copy of the Roman original illustrated in the third supplement of Montfaucon's *Antiquités* (17,19,164). Horace Walpole called it a "pretty small parlour painted in grotesque", on his visit in 1768, but the Duchess of

53

Northumberland described it two years earlier as "painted after the antique but sadly executed".

The room was unfortunately dismantled in 1807, when the walls are recorded as being lath-and-plastered, and subsequently painted grey and white.

However, Brunias' five rectangular landscapes with figures, in their original frames by Sefferin Alken (supplied in May 1761), survived in the house until the 1960s when they were sold to the Victoria and Albert Museum.

Design for one wall of a Book Room 1768
Robert Adam
pen, ink and watercolour
signed and dated
$19\frac{1}{2} \times 24\frac{1}{4}$

This and the following two drawings were part of the unexecuted scheme of 1768 (see nos. 10 and 9 (flap)) to attach square pavilions at the east and west ends of the south front of the main block. These would have contained the book room beyond the Library on the east and the Painted Breakfasting Room beyond the Principal Dressing Room on the west: not unlike the square and circular closets at either end of the long gallery at Syon.

Although the mirrored recesses flanking the chimneypiece seem most improbable for a Book Room, this elevation has to be read in conjunction with drawings of the ceiling, and the door and window walls in the Soane Museum (11:46 and 14:122,123). Taken together these form a complete set of finished drawings for the room, while another set of partly finished drawings from Adam's office, can also be found at the Soane Museum (40:14–16; 11:47–48).

It is of particular interest to relate the drawings of the chimney wall and the ceiling to the equivalent drawing of the library at Kenwood in Middlesex (Soane Museum 14:114), dated only a year earlier. Not only are the ornaments of the alcoves practically identical, but so are the settees within them.

Section of the Chimney Side of a Book Room for Kedleston House

Scale of .... Feet.

Adam Archt. 1768

41–42

Two designs for a Painted Breakfasting Room 1768

Robert Adam

pen, ink and watercolour

signed and dated (one part-signature only)

chimneypiece wall: $21 \times 26\frac{1}{2}$;

ceiling: $26 \times 25\frac{1}{2}$

As with the book room there is an equivalent set of finished drawings now divided between Kedleston and the Soane Museum (door and window walls 14:124,125). The drawings with their intense colours and delicacy of treatment are in complete contrast to the then existing state rooms. The principal apartment, which the room would have adjoined, had only just been completed. To some extent its filigree decoration relates more to the early (1761) Painted Breakfast Room in the family pavilion (nos.38–39), a room whose similar title has caused confusion in the past.

The room was to be 25 feet in diameter with four alcoves interspersed with a doorway, chimneypiece, and two windows. In style the decoration recalls Raphael's Vatican *loggie* more than the latest finds at Herculaneum, despite the consciously "antique" colour scheme of gold and bronze. The medallion over the chimneypiece represents the offering of a chaplet on an altar (the subject perhaps taken from the so-called "Palace of Augustus" illustrated by Charles Cameron – see no.17) while the spandrels of the alcoves are decorated with the Curzon popinjay crest.

At Harewood House there was a circular dressing room (now destroyed), without niches, but otherwise very similar in conception. One of the drawings for it (Soane Museum 11:148) bears an (added) date of 1767.

43
**Cross-section design for the Marble Hall and
Saloon** 1760
Robert Adam
photograph
(courtesy of the Sir John Soane Museum)

This large-scale cross-section in the Soane
Museum (40:3) is of the utmost importance
as there are no surviving drawings at
Kedleston which show Adam's general
design for the Hall and Saloon. His original
concept would otherwise only have been
known from Woolfe and Gandon's
Vitruvius Britannicus engraving of 1767,
which although generally faithful to
Adam's section, lacks much of the detail,
and in any case is not first hand.

Adam made considerable alterations to
the Paine arrangement ; more than can be
briefly described here. But the more
important were : (a) to reduce the forward
projection of the portico to one column
deep, and to step the front wall of the Hall
forward into part of this space ; (b) to light
the Hall from above (in execution the
skylight was altered to three adjacent oval
lights) ; and (c) to scrap the Paine staircase
between the Hall and Saloon, moving the
latter partly back into the body of the
house, and setting the Arch of Constantine
in front as the centrepiece of the south
façade.

The columned Hall is one of the grandest
rooms in the country, and indeed in
Europe. The alabaster columns are of
course the outstanding single feature, and
it is interesting that these were not
originally intended to be fluted. Adam also
provided alternative designs for the
capitals and bases. Happily Lord Scarsdale
chose the more complex (and more
expensive) version (see no.48), but again
these do not appear in the drawing.

The rectangular Hall and circular Saloon
are the equivalent of the "atrium" and
"vestibulum" in a Roman palace or villa, a
theme expounded by Adam in his book on
the *Ruins of Spalatro*, published in 1764,
and the effect of moving from one space to
another is an immensely powerful
experience, in part due to the far greater

height of the rotunda (62 feet, as opposed to 40). The general idea of the coffering, oculus and niches all derive from the Pantheon, one of the buildings often sketched by the architect in Rome, though details are taken from other buildings like the Basilica of Maxentius. On the other hand, the grisaille panels above the niches in the Hall derive from Palladio's reconstruction of the Temple of Mars (4th Book, plate 40), showing that Adam and Lord Scarsdale did not entirely reject the favourite source-book of the previous generation.

The decoration of both the Hall and the Saloon including the plasterwork and most of the paintings, was deferred on financial grounds until the later 1770s and 1780s respectively, the former being executed under the supervision of the clerk of works, Joseph Pickford, using designs by Robert Adam's chief draughtsman, George Richardson. Few major departures from Adam's design were then made, except for the ceiling and chimneypieces in the Hall, and the stoves replacing statues in the alcoves of the Saloon. The Ionic doorcases in the Saloon, with their scagliola pilasters, were also changed at Lord Scarsdale's instigation.

The Saloon was originally intended as a sculpture gallery of casts. Four tall figures stood on pedestals in the alcoves, and eight smaller figures were placed in the rectangular niches, while for many years the Hall had only the two figures of Apollo and Meleager which are still at the south end. When the Saloon was decorated during 1787–89, some of the figures were transferred to the empty niches in the Hall, and some to the Great Staircase. The niches were covered over and the paintings and stucco decorations were provided as they are today.

44
Design for the Hall Floor c.1760
Robert Adam
pen, ink and watercolour
$24\frac{1}{4} \times 35\frac{3}{4}$

This drawing was found in the Kedleston archives among bundles of working drawings. No accounts have been found for laying the floor, but Adam was enquiring about the "scantling" (thickness) as early as 1760. It can be assumed that it was laid in about 1763 after the Hall columns had been erected. The material is Hopton Wood stone with marble inlay. Of the two alternatives presented, the design of intersecting circles at the entrance end was followed, with a few minor additions.

45
Design for the Ceiling of the Marble Hall
1774
George Richardson
pen, ink and watercolour
signed and dated
$19\frac{1}{4} \times 25\frac{1}{2}$

Adam's ceiling design of about 1761 was probably considered somewhat dated by 1774 and Richardson's design, which was executed by Joseph Rose, was more in keeping with the times. The pink and green colour scheme must also have been an innovation, for Adam's entrance halls seem

normally to have been painted in grisaille colours before this date. Appropriately for the Hall, the decoration included military trophies, in the long tradition going back to medieval times, when arms and armour were hung on the walls of the great hall, together with the family's heraldic

achievements – here the popinjay crest of the Curzons. Trophies had previously been intended for other parts of the house including the Sub-Hall and Staircase, but did not materialize.

In 1776 Richardson exhibited at the Royal Academy a drawing entitled "The Ceiling executed in the Grecian Hall at Keddlestone" – probably a large-scale watercolour of the whole ceiling, like the engraved version that appears as plate 48 in his *Book of Ceilings*, published the same year. In the text that accompanies the latter, he explains that "as there are a great many paintings in Chiaro Oscuro, from the antique, and from Homer's Iliad, on the sides of the Hall, it was judged improper to introduce any historical pictures in this ceiling; Grecian trophies of stucco are therefore adopted, as proper accompaniments to the pictures . . .".

Part of the Ceiling of the Hall, with the Cove extended upon a Straight Line.

George Richardson 1774.

46
Cross-section design for the Marble Hall
1774
George Richardson
pen, ink and watercolour
signed and dated
$25 \times 37\frac{1}{4}$

The drawing is a particularly beautiful one, showing how George Richardson came to be employed as chief draughtsman by the Adam brothers for so many years, accompanying James on his Grand Tour in 1760–63.

At this time the Hall had no stucco or painted decoration and it was Richardson who provided the detailed designs. There were no major changes to Adam's designs except in the ceiling, doors and chimney-pieces. The columns were only fluted in 1775, but the more elaborate bases and capitals (see no.48) are not shown, implying that Richardson had not yet visited Kedleston at the time this design was drawn up.

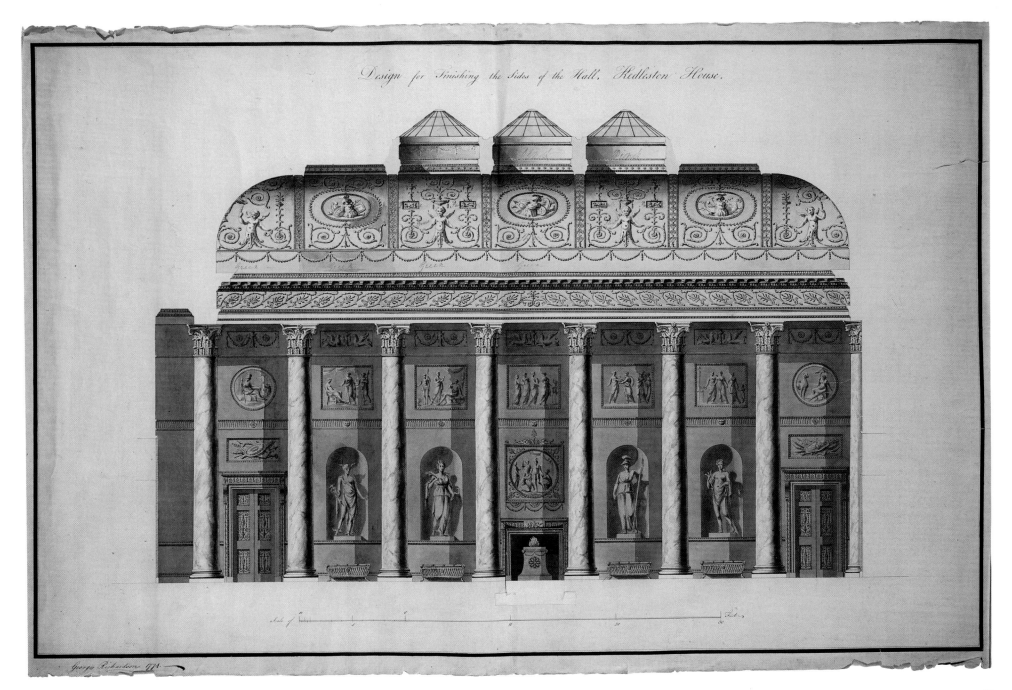

George Richardson 1771

61

47
Design for a painted panel in the Saloon
1768
William Hamilton
watercolour
signed
$8\frac{1}{4} \times 21$

William Hamilton (1751–1801) was the son
of one of Robert Adam's Scottish
assistants, and having shown promise as a
painter was sent by Adam to Rome at an
early age. After studying under Antonio
Zucchi, he became one of the leading
native history-painters of the day.
Hamilton was responsible for the four large
paintings of Roman ruins above the doors
in the Saloon at Kedleston, painted about
1787 and replacing an earlier series of
paintings by Morland, after Rubens. But
this sketch is for one of the four thinner
panels above the niches – eventually filled
with scenes from British history in *grisaille*
by Biagio Rebecca. One of the 1st Lord
Scarsdale's small notebooks, dating from
1768, gives the subjects for these earlier
panels (probably never executed) as "A
Persian Caravan Marching", "A Caravan
halting and refreshing itself", "Feast of
Bairam – Turkish women go abroad", and
finally "Carnival at Venice".

48
Working drawing for a Corinthian Capital in the Marble Hall 1761
Robert Adam
pen and ink with pencil underlay
$47\frac{1}{2} \times 48$

The Kedleston collection is particularly rich in full-scale working drawings, produced by the draughtsmen in Adam's office (but under his direct supervision), and sent down to the masons, carvers and other craftsmen at Kedleston. Over a hundred of them survive, all on the same rough paper as this drawing, and showing the wear and tear inevitable through frequent use.

The Corinthian capitals in the hall are particularly splendid; their design was taken from the three remaining columns of what was then called the temple of Jupiter Stator (Ware's edition of Palladio, 4th book, 69), and which are still standing in the Roman Forum. Adam wrote to Lord Scarsdale on 23 April 1761 to say that he was sending the design of the capital by waggon. Soon after, on 8 May, he continued "The Capital I sent down for the Hall is reckoned the finest of all the Antient Corinthian ones. But it is impossible for me to determine whether your Lop will think the additional Beauty equal to the additional expence, as your Lop does not say how much Mr Hall asks of addition. But at the same time I should prefer it much to the other for Inside Columns if I was building for myself."

Lord Scarsdale chose the more beautiful and expensive capital. The principal carver James Gravener spent nearly eight days carving a model, and the carpenters glued it up. The seventy-two faces of the capitals cost nine pounds each, totalling £648.

49
Design for a Chimneypiece in the Hall 1775
George Richardson
pen, ink and wash
dated, signature now removed
$12\frac{3}{4} \times 12\frac{3}{4}$

This drawing is a very accurate representation of the two white marble chimneypieces in the Hall as executed, perhaps by the carver George Moneypenny, with the Curzon arms and supporters in their central tablets. The fireplace surround closely matches that in Richardson's *New Collection of Chimney Pieces*, published in 1781, and other features of the drawing associate it with him. However the drawing of the fire basket has been pasted into the central space and it has not yet been possible to prove whether it is by Adam or Richardson.

The fire baskets were repaired on several occasions during the 19th century, and although in need of some restoration are in remarkably good condition. It is possible that they were made by Thomas Blockley of Birmingham, who supplied grates for the house in the 1760s and who received larger payments than usual in 1776–77. Blockley had links with Matthew Boulton, who could have collaborated with him, perhaps supplying the chased brasswork.

Design of a Chimney-piece for the Hall, Kedleston House.
(executed)

1775 — Scale of Feet

50
View of Kedleston c.1710
attributed to Jan Griffier I
oil on canvas
43 × 71

The viewpoint is from the south-south-east of the house. The landscape setting with the foothills of the Peak in the background is obviously exaggerated, but the house and church and their immediate surroundings are quite accurately depicted as they must have been before 1721, when Bridgeman's formal gardens shown in the plan (no.53) began to be laid out. The portrayal of the house itself seems to accord with the ground plan of the Smith of Warwick building (no.51), somewhat distorted on the extreme right-hand corner.

The attribution to the Dutch-born artist, Jan Griffier (1625–1718), is based on the very similar Rhenish landscapes seen in the background of his views of Syon and Hampton Court, painted about 1710, and his somewhat earlier view of Sudbury Hall in Derbyshire, not far away from Kedleston. The large tree on the left, used as *staffage*, can be almost exactly paralleled in a panoramic view of Nottingham (now in the Nottingham Castle Museum), also attributed to Griffier (J. Harris, figs. 130–33). A "Landskip with Ruins" by Griffier was bought by Sir Nathaniel Curzon, 4th Bart., at Sir James Thornhill's sale in 1734/35.

51
Survey Plan of the Old House at Kedleston
1758
attributed to Jason Harris
pen, ink and wash
$12 \times 14\frac{1}{2}$

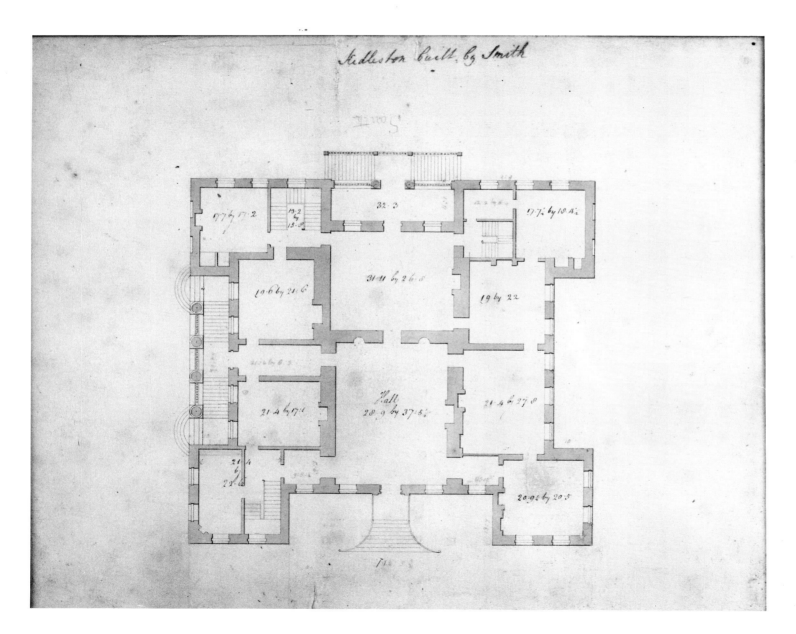

This ground-floor plan of the early 18th-century house built by Sir Nathaniel Curzon, 2nd Bart., is inscribed at the top "Kedleston built by Smith" (in the 1st Lord Scarsdale's hand) – a reference to the architect Francis Smith of Warwick, who designed it in about 1700. The drawing was probably made in September 1758 when the London carpenter Jason Harris was paid for going to survey the house with Matthew Brettingham, not long before its demolition.

The rectangular plan with corner pavilions derives ultimately from Robert Hooke's Ragley Hall in Warwickshire, and is rare in Smith's repertoire. A later plan made by Admiral Henry Curzon, younger son of the 1st Lord Scarsdale, gives the names of all the rooms: the Saloon beyond the Hall (in the centre of the south front); the State Bedroom and Dressing Room in the south-west corner, and Withdrawing Room and Cabinet in the north-west; the Parlour and Breakfast Room behind the loggia on the east front, and the Study in the south-east corner. The plan conforms reasonably well with Griffier's picture of the house (no.50).

Literature: Colvin, 9

Design for a Canal with Cascades c.1725
attributed to Charles Bridgeman
$10\frac{3}{4} \times 27$

Charles Bridgeman, the Royal gardener, was employed by Sir John Curzon at Kedleston in the 1720s – "Mr Bridgeman's man" received a guinea in 1722, and Bridgeman himself the large sum of 60 guineas in 1726, while many of the plants were supplied by Joseph Carpenter, George London's successor at the Brompton nurseries (Willis, 33,87). Bridgeman and James Gibbs very often worked in partnership (for instance at Wimpole, Houghton, Gubbins and Badminton), and the former may well have recommended him to Curzon.

The canal appears in the survey map showing the park before 1758 (no.53), with the Octagon Pond north of the old house on the other side of the turnpike road. The general situation would have appeared quite impressive to the passing traveller with the formal gardens leading up to the house.

The drawing shows a series of weirs, beside each of which the fall is shown, usually about three feet. A line of trees is indicated on each side of the canal, also appearing in a section at the edge of the drawing. The latter shows the water to be 60 feet wide with walks of 20 feet on each side. Sight lines are shown as from the house to the lower circular pond.

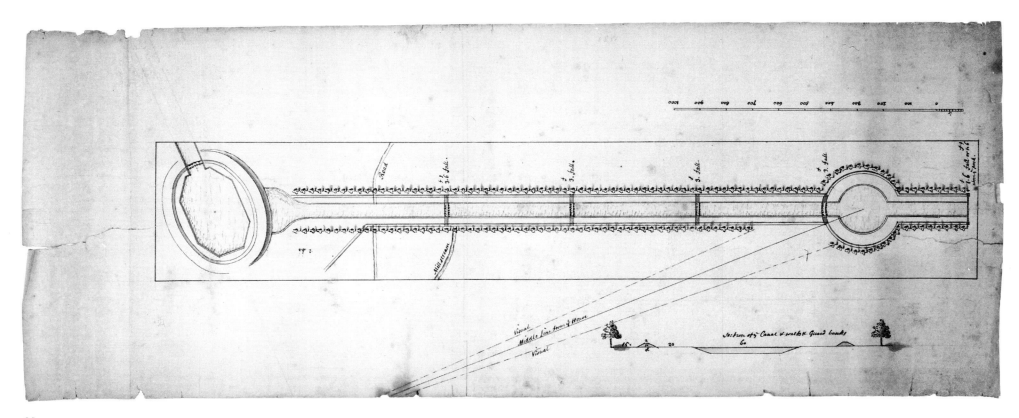

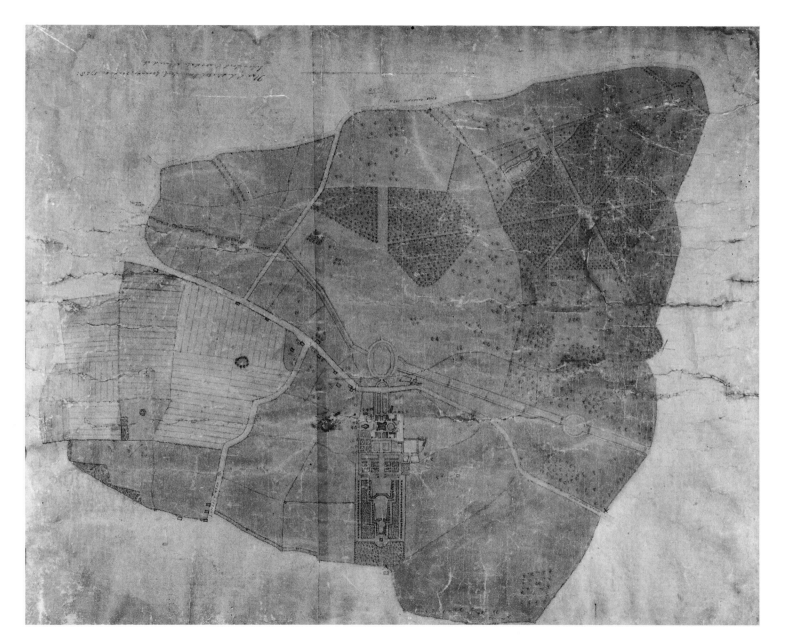

53
Survey Map of Kedleston House and Park
before 1758
pen, ink and wash
29 × 33½

The map is inscribed in the 1st Lord Scarsdale's hand, at top left (as exhibited): "Plan of Kedleston House, Park, Grounds, Roads &c 1758: before Lord Scarsdale altered it". It records the appearance of the landscape at Kedleston after about 1735, following major expenditure by Sir John Curzon in 1721–26 – using the Royal gardener, Charles Bridgeman – and by his brother, Sir Nathaniel Curzon, 4th Bart., in 1734. The public turnpike road is shown passing only about 160 yards north of the house; it was diverted in 1760 via the rond-point (upper right).

Just above the point where the turnpike passes the house, Bridgeman's octagon pond can be seen, with a canal descending to the right through a series of weirs to a circular pond. The village was not a cohesive affair, but was scattered along the turnpike to the north-west (left) of the house; only the parsonage was at all near the house, to the north of the church. The stables lay south-east of the house, and the formal gardens rose up the slope to the south.

Two watercolours of scenes in Kedleston Park by Mrs Delany, made in 1746, give an idea of its somewhat confined charms. One of them probably shows the end of the canal (near the western end of the present upper lake), and the other Harepit Hill – whose summit is marked on the map with a ring of trees – with some of the old village houses on the road below.

54–55
Two Views of Kedleston c.1780
attributed to George Cuitt
oil on canvas
36 × 66

These two pictures, previously attributed
to Joseph Farington, have close affinities
with the Yorkshire country house views of
George Cuitt (1743–1818), like those of
Easby Hall, Aske Hall and Forcett Park
(J. Harris, figs.329–31) – all displaying the
same prominent white highlights. Cuitt
was himself a Yorkshireman, who had been
sent to Italy by another of Robert Adam's
major patrons, Sir Lawrence Dundas.

The two views are taken from the south-
west and north-west respectively: the
former showing a yacht on the lake to the
right of Adam's south front (perhaps the
"Ship" supplied by J. Denoyer in 1760 at a
cost of £210, or one of a number of other
boats bought in subsequent years); and the
latter showing the north front with Adam's
bridge on the left, and his fishing room-
boat house on the right.

56
Survey Map of Kedleston 1764
George Ingman
pen and ink on vellum
signed and dated
35 × 43

This is one of a series of survey maps of the Curzon family estates. Apart from the centre and lower lakes (to the right), it gives a fair idea of the planting only five years after Robert Adam had begun to remodel it for the 1st Lord Scarsdale. In the words of William Bray, whose *Sketch of a Tour into Derbyshire* was published in 1783, "the village is removed (not destroyed, as is too often done), the road is thrown to a considerable distance, out of sight of the house, the scanty stream is encreased into a large piece of water, and the ground disposed in the finest order".

The Long Walk, with a "fosse" or ha-ha on each side, proceeding west from the house, was part-completed by that date. The hermitage in its path (no.73) was certainly ready and thatched. The turnpike road, previously in front of the house, now passed through the rond-point (upper right) where Adam's north lodge (no.63) was already standing. The sulphur bath (no.80), built in 1759–61, is shown just above the lower island. However, Adam's bridge and cascade (no.66), and his fishing room-boat house (nos.67–69) were yet to come (1770–71), as probably was the new village lodge, although they all appear on the map.

The upper lake, above the bridge, was probably complete before 1760, but Bridgeman's old ponds and canal remained below the bridge until the principal lakes were dug in the 1770s. At the top of the map is the Ireton garden laid out in the 1740s by Mary Assheton (Lord Scarsdale's mother) on the neighbouring Little Ireton estate, which the family had acquired in 1721. Part of this garden, which achieved some fame, still survives, and in particular the gothic temple built by Lord Scarsdale in 1759 (for which a drawing – not by Adam – survives in the Soane Museum, 40:55).

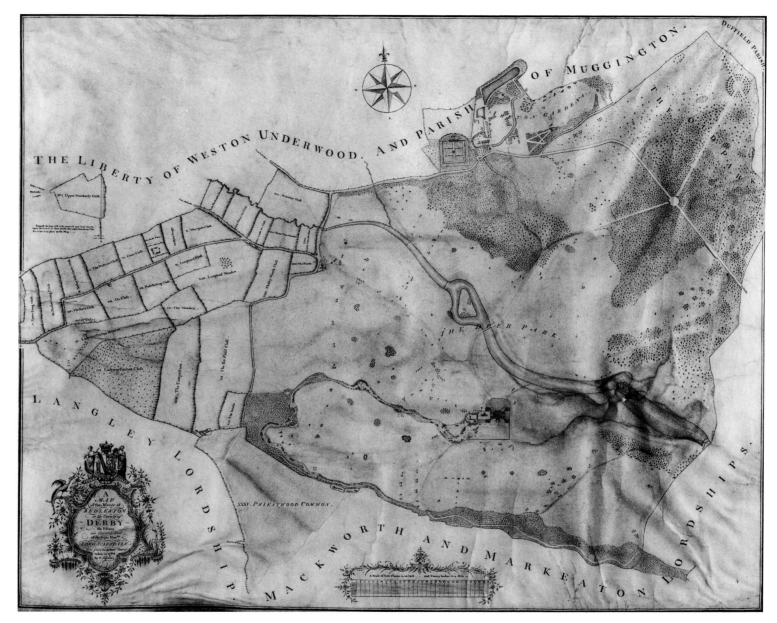

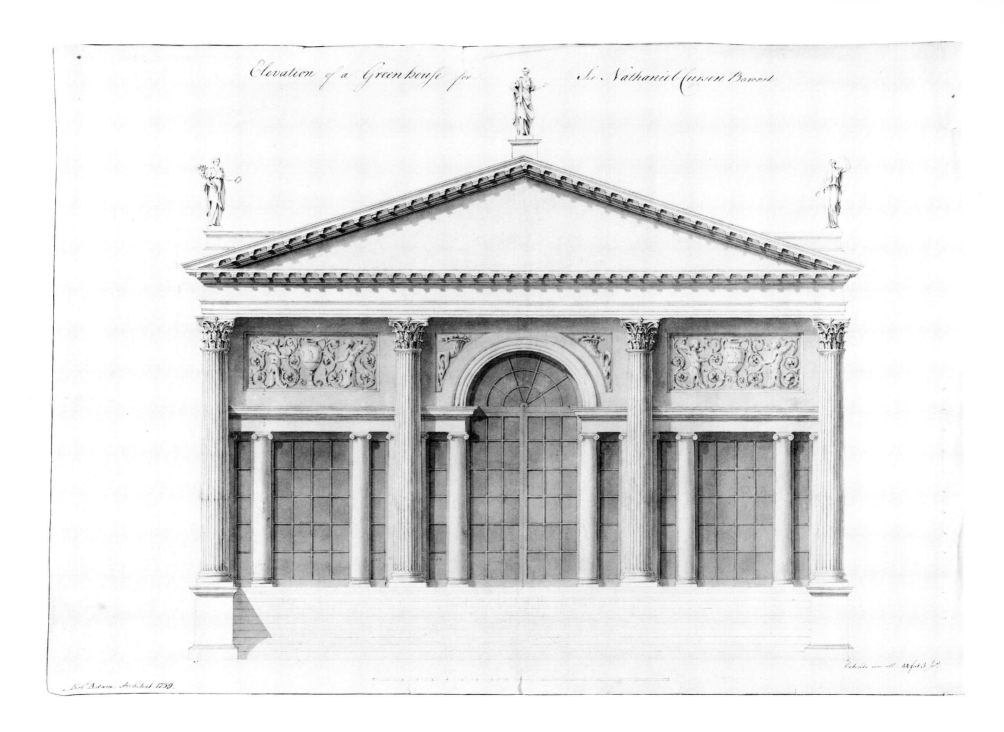

Elevation of a Greenhouse for Sir Nathaniel Curzen Baronet

Rob.t Adam Architect 1759.

70

57
Design for a Greenhouse 1759
Robert Adam
pen, ink and wash
signed and dated
$19\frac{1}{2} \times 26\frac{1}{2}$

Adam provided a set of four drawings for
this building, all signed and dated 1759.
They included a plan, one end elevation
and a section showing flues; a similar set is
in the Soane Museum (40:37–40). Another
identical elevation (32:65) is headed
"Green House executed at General Blands
[at Gordon House, Isleworth, Middlesex]
and to be done at Sir Nath Curzons" –
Humphry Bland having the distinction of
being Adam's earliest patron on his return
from Italy.

However, Kedleston had to wait for its
more prosaic greenhouse, designed by
George Richardson in 1799, built in
1800–1, and moved about a hundred yards
in 1922.

58
Design for Bentley Well c.1763
Robert Adam
pen and sepia ink
$7\frac{1}{2} \times 12\frac{1}{2}$

This small pedimented building, a hundred
yards beyond the bridge, to the left of the
drive when approaching the house, was
known alternatively as Bentley Well or the
Lion's Mouth – the former name evidently
deriving from a steward named Bentley
who died in the 1740s, and whose
tombstone can still be seen in the
churchyard at Kedleston. It covers a
plentiful spring which flows to the fishing
room-boat house. The accounts refer in
April 1763 to the carpenters for
"centering" (for the arch). Both the
draughtsmanship and inscription are
typical of Adam's early drawings, although
this is evidently a hurried sketch; he was of
course fully in charge of the landscape at
Kedleston at this date. In a notebook of
1772 Lord Scarsdale wrote himself a
memorandum to plant "Weeping Willow &
draw a Rose over Bentley Well".

A Design of a Small Building over the Spring of Water at Kedleston

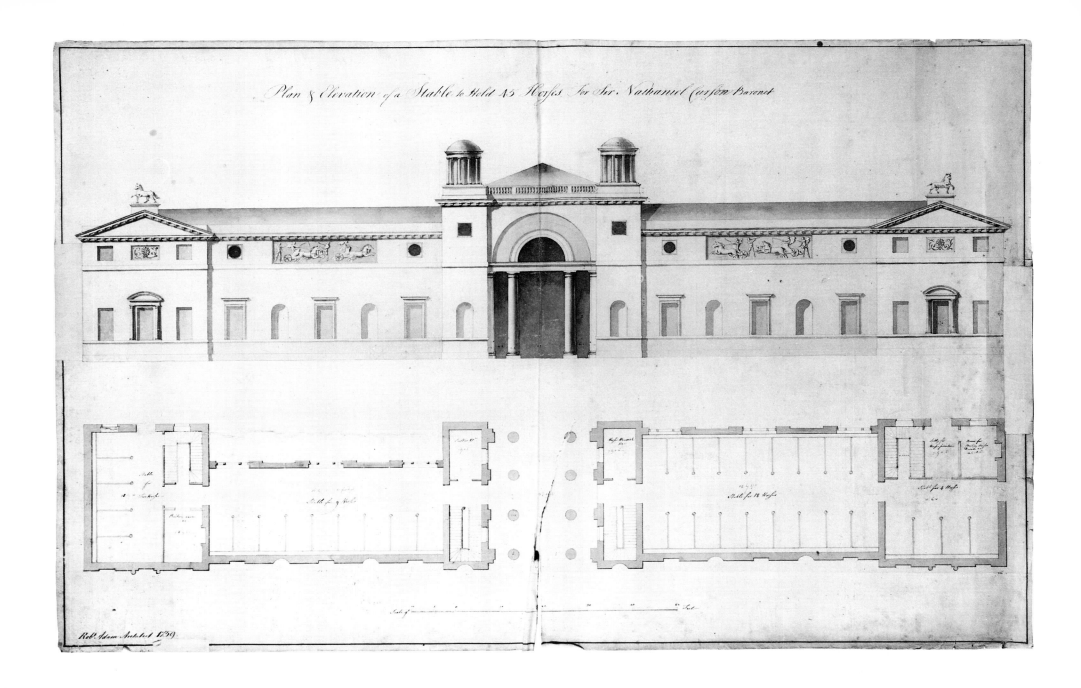

Plan & Elevation of a Stable to Hold 45 Horses for Sir Nathaniel Curson Baronet

Rob.t Adam Architect 1759

59
Design for a Stable Block 1759
Robert Adam
pen, ink and wash
signed and dated
$24\frac{3}{4} \times 38\frac{1}{2}$

Temporary stables were built in 1759–60,
no doubt to replace those which were
demolished to make way for the new house
and pavilions – and the carpenter Jason
Harris was probably responsible for these.

Adam wrote in July 1759 (no doubt after
his spring visit) to say that he was sending
"the plan of the stables", and these designs
were used as the basis for Samuel Wyatt's,
built in 1767–69. The equivalent drawing
at the Soane Museum (40:26) lacks much of
the ornamental detail, such as the bas-
reliefs of chariot races, behind which lay
the hay-lofts.

60
Design for the Interior of the Stables 1767
Samuel Wyatt
pen, ink and wash
$14\frac{1}{4} \times 20\frac{3}{4}$

Samuel Wyatt was engaged first as master
carpenter and then as clerk of the works at
Kedleston from 1760 to about 1768,
marrying the daughter of Lord Scarsdale's
land agent, Ann Sherwin, in 1765. His
contact with Adam, and practical
experience in the designing and
construction of a major building, were to
be of the greatest importance for his future
career, and the stables at Kedleston can be
considered his first independent building of
any importance. This design is one of six
drawings bound in a soft marbled cover,
consisting of two plans, an elevation and
three sections.

The main elevation was a much simpler
arrangement than Adam's but it retained
the projecting pedimented end blocks and
central opening. The most important
change in the plan was to reduce the depth
from two to one stall, and to regain the
capacity by extending the right (west) end
projection to the rear so as to accom-
modate the 20-stall stable shown here. It is
a splendid groin-vaulted room, virtually
untouched since it was built in 1767–69.

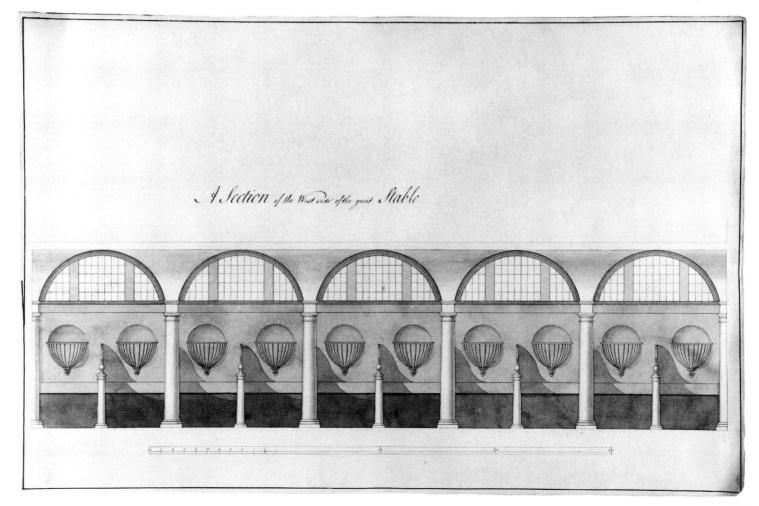

A Section of the West side of the great Stable

61
Sketch for Landscaping the Park 1759
Robert Adam
pen and sepia ink, and watercolour
$10\frac{1}{2} \times 16\frac{1}{2}$

In December 1758 Adam was introduced to Sir Nathaniel Curzon, 4th Baronet, by his friend Lord Charles Hay. Curzon had succeeded his father less than a month before, and was busily planning his new house at Kedleston. In his letter of 11 December to his brother James, describing his meeting with Curzon, Adam went on to say that he had "got the intire managdement of his Grounds put into my hands with full powers as to Temples Bridges Seats & Cascades. So that as it only is Seven Miles round you may guess the play of Genius & Scope for Invention. A noble piece of water, a man resolved to spare no

Expence, with £10,000 a Year, Good Temper'd & having taste himself for the Arts and little for Game." A few days later Adam returned to Curzon's London house, carrying "many drawings and amongst others the Nabobs Palace" – with which Sir Nathaniel was so delighted that he swore "if he had £300,000 he would begin it directly". Robert was "to go to Derbyshire as soon in the Spring as I can". It is almost certain that he made this and the following sketch (no.62) at this time, both of them bound into a thin sketchbook with a soft marbled cover, together with a rough plan of the pleasure grounds west and south of the house which can be related to the 1764 Ingman plan (no.56).

This drawing seems to have been taken from north of the island in Ingman's plan, looking south, over the upper lake in the foreground, to a large building on a new site below Harepit Hill, sometimes thought to be the "Nabob's Palace" mentioned in Adam's letter. In fact, the latter is more likely to have been a design based on the Baths of Diocletian, which the architect had drawn up in Rome in 1756 (Fleming, fig.48), and this drawing may simply represent a very large stable block, to be built round a courtyard, with a central spire of a type found on several Scottish stables, like Sir James Clerk's at Penicuik. The spire is certainly curious, and may seem at odds with Adam's usual neo-classical style, but similar features can be found in several of his *capricii* made in Rome in 1757, as well as his sketches of Romanesque basilicas like the Santo at Padua (Fleming, figs. 74,76,77).

62
Sketch for Landscaping the Park 1759
Robert Adam
pen and sepia ink, and watercolour
11 × 33

The view seems to be taken from a point just beyond the ha-ha to the south-west of the house, looking west-north-west. On the far right can be seen the palatial stables proposed in the previous drawing, with Harepit Hill above, crowned with a clump of trees. Three different temples or "eyecatchers" are shown, all of them indicated on the circuit walk shown in Adam's rough plan of the pleasure grounds, and on the Ingman survey of 1764 (no.56). Only the Pantheon-type building in the centre is shown differently – as a rotunda, without a portico – on the plan.

The influence of Charles-Louis Clérisseau, the French artist whom Adam met in Florence, and who became his drawing master, is abundantly clear, and the idea of a panoramic view showing proposed buildings in a natural landscape is of great originality for its time, foreshadowing the "Red Books" of Humphry Repton.

76

63
Design for the North Lodge 1759
Robert Adam
pen and sepia ink and watercolour
$14 \times 21\frac{1}{4}$

There are several pen-and-ink drawings for this lodge in the Soane Museum showing alternative Doric and Corinthian orders, but all have solid main doors, with either doors or windows each side. This coloured drawing (the only one to show the building in its landscape setting) depicts iron gates, for which there are also drawings in the Soane Museum (40:49), and appears to come from the same sketchbook as nos.61 and 62.

In execution the Doric order was adopted, as here, with iron gates to a slightly simpler design made by Benjamin Yates. Side windows were provided, the bottoms of which have subsequently been lowered. The lodge was one of the first buildings by Adam to be completed at Kedleston (1760–62); it stands at the rond-point on the diverted turnpike road, and was described in the c.1778 Kedleston catalogue as being based on the "Arch of Octavia".

64
View of Kedleston from the East c.1759
Robert Adam
pen, sepia ink and watercolour
$4\frac{3}{4} \times 13$

This is a composite drawing with the side elevation of the house cut out and pasted on to a landscape sketch, showing Harepit Hill to the right of the family pavilion. In July 1760 Adam sent Curzon a sketch of the east end of the house showing the positions of windows in the attic storey, and referring to the family wing cutting off the view from the attic rooms of the main block. Although it is unlikely that it was this drawing, which shows blank windows on the back of the quadrant (a feature Adam was discouraging in his accompanying letter), it may be of the same date, since the pavilion is shown as if already built, with the main block (as yet unexecuted) differently treated. One important difference between this elevation and the appearance of the house today is that the ground floor of the quadrant was never rusticated.

Sir William Chambers is often credited with being the first to show proposed buildings in a natural landscape setting (for instance at Kew), and it is interesting to find Adam experimenting along the same lines at very much the same time.

65
Design for a Bridge 1758
Michael Henry Spang
pen and ink, and watercolour
signed and dated
$5\frac{1}{2} \times 7\frac{1}{2}$

Spang, the Danish sculptor, seems to have been involved in a variety of odd tasks for Nathaniel Curzon in the late 1750s, as well as later carving statues and tablets for chimneypieces in the new house. Before Adam's arrival on the scene, he may well have acted as draughtsman for some of Curzon's own architectural and decorative schemes. His drawing for the bridge is somewhat amateur, but has rather more sophisticated sculptural ornament – which may represent his own contribution.

66
Design for the Bridge and Cascade 1759
Robert Adam
pen, sepia ink and watercolour
$16\frac{1}{2} \times 21\frac{1}{2}$

The bridge had a dual purpose. It was and is one of the finest viewpoints in the park; after the descent from the North Lodge the bridge rises to give a magnificent view of the house in its setting. It is also a splendid eyecatcher among the lakes and trees as seen from the house: a view which was obviously of the greatest importance to Lord Scarsdale.

There are several drawings showing a single-arch bridge, of which one in the Soane Museum is signed and dated 1761 (40:41); the cascade was a feature of them all. By 1764 designs were produced for a more splendid three-arch bridge, which was built in 1770–71.

On the verso of this drawing are two long Latin inscriptions, evidently intended to be carved on the central tablets on each side, below the balustrade. The drawing appears to have been torn out of the same sketch-book that contained nos.62, 63 and 75.

Spang fecit.

Design of a Ceiling for the Fishing Room at Kedleston.

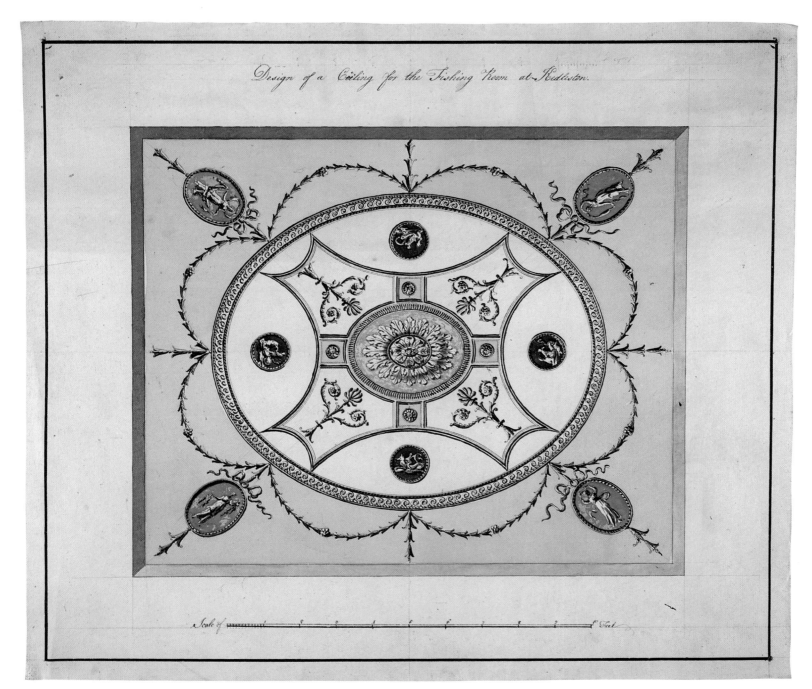

Scale of Feet

80

Two designs for the Fishing Room c.1769
Robert Adam
pen, ink and wash
wall elevations: $33 \times 25\frac{1}{4}$; ceiling $18\frac{1}{4} \times 20\frac{1}{2}$

The fishing-room-cum-boathouse-cum-cold-bath, which Adam designed for Lord Scarsdale, must be one of the most fascinating park buildings in the country. It was constructed on two levels on the slope down to the southern edge of the upper lake, opposite the island. At park level is the fishing room with Adam's decorative stucco, and wall paintings, the latter of fish, seascapes and anglers. The ceiling design with its medallions treated like antique cameos, their backgrounds picked out in vivid colours, is one of the most charming of all those he produced for Kedleston. A seated figure of Venus raised on a pedestal now occupies a niche, in place of the fountain, shown in the drawing. From the Venetian window one could presumably fish in comfort.

A double stair leads down from the fishing room to the semi-circular cold bath and to boathouses on either side.

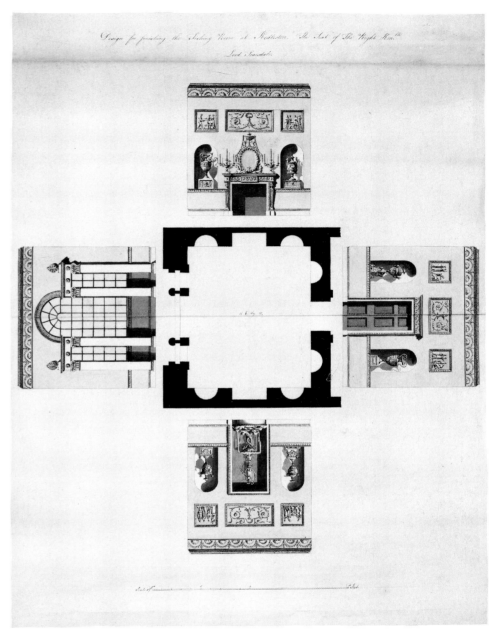

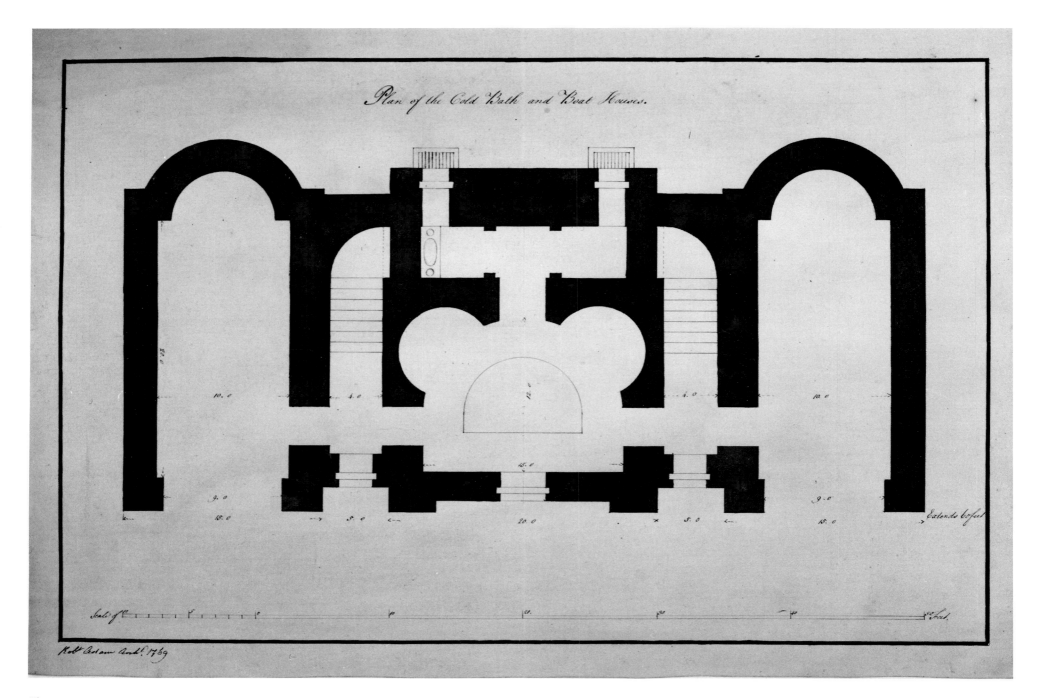

Plan of the Cold Bath and Boat Houses.

69
**Plan of the Cold Bath and Boat Houses
under the Fishing Room** 1769
Robert Adam
pen, ink and wash
$17 \times 25\frac{1}{4}$

While all is delicacy and refinement in the
fishing room above (if in need of some
restoration), the descent is into pure
Piranesian architecture. Although the
scale is small, the impact can be described
as one of the major experiences at
Kedleston, and it is very much to be hoped
that the building will one day be opened to
the public.

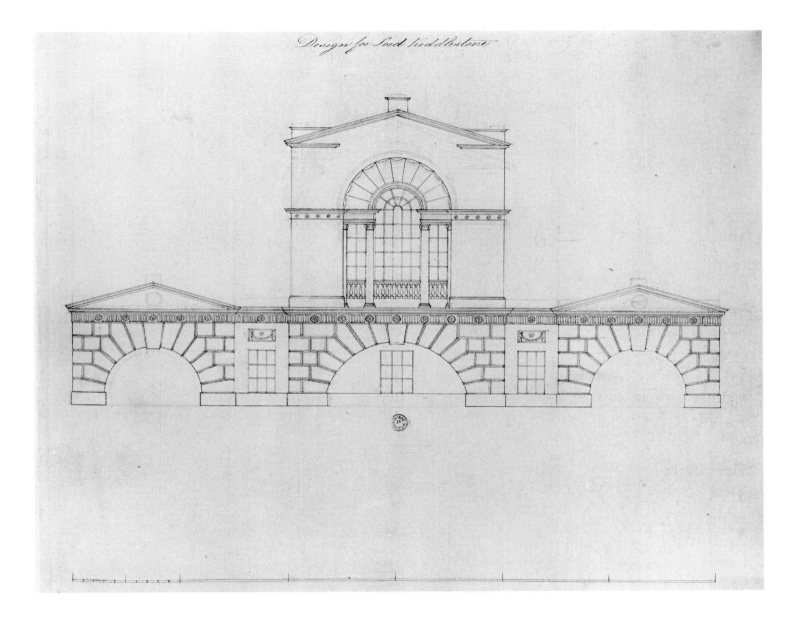

(Right) Design for the north front of the
Fishing Room and Boat House, in the Sir
John Soane Museum. The inscription,
mistakenly referring to "Lord
Keddlestone" instead of Lord Scarsdale, is
in the hand of one of Adam's office
draughtsmen

Two designs for a Grotto or Rock Room
early 1760s
Robert Adam
pen and ink, with pencil underlay
wall elevation: $6\frac{1}{4} \times 8$;
cross-section with cupola $10\frac{1}{2} \times 5\frac{1}{4}$

These drawings appear to have been made for a subterranean "rock room" planned for the garden at Ireton (see no.56), where Lord Scarsdale's mother, Mary Assheton, had already constructed a grotto in the sandpit beyond the farm. The decoration, with a dado based on Roman sarcophagi, and incorporating cinerary urns, is strongly reminiscent of the long gallery at Syon (cf. Soane Museum 1:162 and 39:2).

Lord Scarsdale's first inscription under the wall elevation reads "This may do very well for the inside finishing of the Rock room in ye Pit near the Garden." However, in a second inscription (added later) he writes "something of this sort for the room under the Greenhouse [word erased] in the Small West Pavilion". The south-west pavilion of the house, as originally planned by Adam, was to contain a chapel and a greenhouse (the latter on the principal floor) and this design would have suited the room below.

It is suggested that in 1768, when these large pavilions had been abandoned, and when Adam was proposing smaller square pavilions joined at each end of the south front, Lord Scarsdale erased the words "under the Greenhouse" and substituted "in the Small West Pavilion" (i.e. under the Painted Breakfasting Room, see no.41). The semicircular lunettes shown here would have perfectly suited the therm window shown under the left-hand pavilion in no.10.

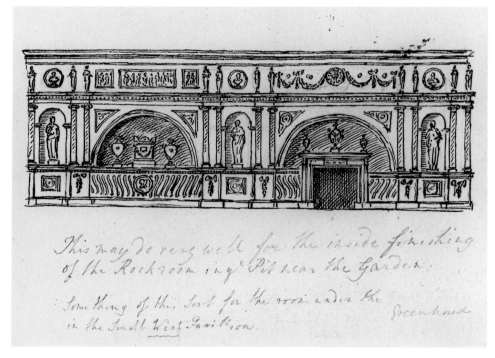

72
Design for a Grotto early 1760s
attributed to Robert Adam
pencil
$9 \times 8\frac{1}{4}$

This little pencil sketch shows a ''temple''
on the rock above the entrance to a cave or
grotto, which exactly matches the cupola
of the ''rock room'' shown in no.71. An
inscription in the 1st Lord Scarsdale's
hand – ''This Design for the Pit on the left
hand of the Garden'' – also suggests that it
depicts the rock under which Adam's
subterranean room was to be built in the
garden at Ireton – with the cave-opening
presumably leading into it.

73
Design for the Hermitage c.1760
attributed to Robert Adam
pen, ink and watercolour
$5\frac{1}{2} \times 10\frac{1}{2}$

The hermitage was constructed in the
pleasure ground in 1761–62, at a time when
Adam was in full charge of all the building
works at Kedleston. The solid part of the
structure survives in the Long Walk, just a
half-mile west of the south front of the
house. It was re-thatched in 1860, and
probably again since then, and could be
satisfactorily restored.

74
Design for the Hexagon Temple c.1775
attributed to George Richardson
pen, ink and wash
$21\frac{1}{4} \times 14\frac{1}{2}$

No record has been found for building this
temple in the pleasure ground, only a short
distance to the west of the house, but the
draughtsmanship and scale are typical of
Richardson. In 1775 he was much involved
in the decoration of the Hall (see no.46)
and produced several other drawings. The
pencil inscriptions at the bottom in the 1st
Lord Scarsdale's hand read "Must not
exceed twelve feet to the very top, and the
Pillasters to be ten diameters – Ten feet
would be high enough", and "Summer
House in Pleasure Ground". In 1922 the
building was moved about 200 yards to the
south.

75
Design for the Pheasant House 1759
Robert Adam
pencil, with pen and sepia ink and
watercolour overlay
$14\frac{1}{4} \times 19\frac{3}{4}$

Adam's pheasant house was to have been a
most attractive re-modelling of an
apparently very ordinary existing
structure. The ground plan is drawn on the
rock below the elevation, but two more
formal drawings at Kedleston, signed and
dated 1760, show a rather different internal
arrangement, also omitting the ornament
in the pediment. The plan of the upper
storey has doors leading on to the roofs of
the porch and the two semi-circular
porticoes. Presumably these were to
provide platforms from which to shoot
pheasants. The Amalienburg in the park of
the Nymphenburg Palace, Munich,
designed by Cuvilliés (1734–39) had a dome
with similar platforms round it. As Adam
returned from Italy via Germany in 1757,
and was certainly at Augsburg, it is
possible that he saw the building, and was
inspired by it.

The drawing appears to have been torn
from the same sketchbook that contained
nos. 62, 63 and 66.

76–77
Two designs for a View Tower 1760
Robert Adam
pen, ink and wash
signed and dated
elevation: $26\frac{1}{2} \times 16\frac{1}{2}$; cross-section
$25\frac{1}{2} \times 19\frac{1}{2}$

In Adam's first surviving letter to
Nathaniel Curzon in July 1759, he refers to
beginning the design of the tower, and a
year later he sent a model of it (would that
it had survived!). The tower was never
executed, but it would have been an
imposing structure 84 feet 7 inches high
and varying up to 50 feet in width: a
classical version of the 78-foot high Gothic
Brizlee Tower at Alnwick, which he
designed for the Duke of Northumberland
in 1777. Adam provided seven drawings for
the view tower at Kedleston, all signed and
dated 1760.

Rob.t Adam Architect 1760

Rob.t Adam Architect 1760

Design of a Milliarium (for Sir Nath. Curzon Baronet)

TO
KEDLESTON HOUSE
1 MILE.

Ten feet

Robert Adam Architect 1760.

Design for a Milestone or "Milliarium" 1760
Robert Adam
pen, ink and wash
signed and dated
$19\frac{1}{2} \times 12\frac{1}{2}$

Adam reported in July 1760 that he had
begun the drawing of the milliarium, and
there are two related designs in the Soane
Museum (40:51,52): one identical, and the
other with spiral fluting above the tablet.
On another free-hand sketch "ROAD TO
LEEDS" appears on the tablet, which
suggests a connection with Harewood.
    The milliarium was certainly begun, as
brickwork was provided for the
foundation, and the masons also supplied
"circular moulded work"; but nothing
appears to survive. Samuel Wyatt later
adapted the design of the plinth for the
much larger pedestal which now supports
Joseph Wilton's Medicean lion in the
pleasure ground.

79
Design for a Deercote 1767
Samuel Wyatt
pen, ink and wash
$20\frac{1}{2} \times 14\frac{3}{4}$

This extraordinary elevation has a
matching plan, showing a large square
court, with the minaret rising from the
centre. The drawing can be safely
attributed to Wyatt, but the inspiration
undoubtedly came from a 17th-century
volume in Lord Scarsdale's library, George
Wheler's *Journey into Greece*, published in
1682 (vol.II, plate 3, p.187, entitled
"Achmet's Mosck"). Needless to say it was
not built.

The "deer park" is defined in Ingman's
map of 1764 (no.56), though it is uncertain
where exactly the deercote was to be
situated. Deer continued to be kept at
Kedleston until 1942, and it is to be hoped
that a herd may one day be re-established.

A New Design of a Deercote for the Rt. Honble Ld. Scarsdale.

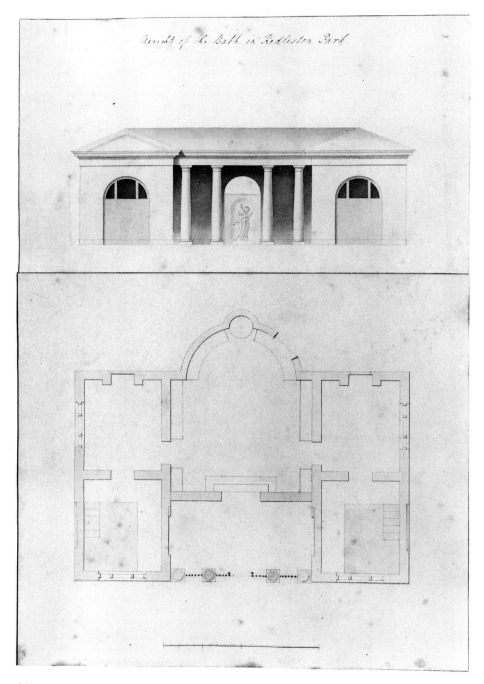

Upright of the Bath in Kedleston Park.

80

Design for the Bath House c.1759
attributed to Jason Harris
pen, ink and wash (on two sheets, both
trimmed)
$11\frac{3}{4} \times 7$

The bath house built over a sulphur spring
in the park at Kedleston, just to the north
of the lower lake (see no.56) has no known
connection with Adam, and was being
constructed by Jason Harris, the London
carpenter, as early as June 1759, when
Swithland slates were supplied for it. Up
until the spring of that year, when Adam
paid his first visit to Kedleston, James
Paine was in charge of all the building
works, but this drawing cannot be given to
him on grounds of draughtsmanship or by
virtue of the inscription. Harris himself is a
more likely candidate, given the
handwriting of the inscription, and

payments to him for drawing columns and
entablatures, and making other
architectural surveys and designs. The
building appears to have been executed
largely to this model though it was halved
in depth during restoration in 1922. The
plunge baths shown on each side may have
been intended to separate the sexes. It is
possible that the apsidal central room was
not intended to be roofed; restoration to its
original plan would be highly desirable.

The inn was built on the newly diverted
turnpike road to designs by Adam in
1760–62 to provide accommodation for
people visiting the sulphur bath, and it
achieved some renown as a miniature spa.
According to William Bray's *Sketch of a
Tour into Derbyshire* (1783) it had "the
virtues of the *Harrowgate* water . . . but will
not bear carriage".

81
Design for a Windmill 1758
attributed to Jason Harris
pen, ink and wash
21 × 14

Jason Harris, the London carpenter,
charged a guinea in 1758 for going to
Coney, near St. Albans, to measure a
windmill. This is followed in the accounts
by a payment of $1\frac{1}{2}$ guineas for drawing a
plan and elevation of a windmill. Had it
been built, it would probably have stood
on Harepit Hill north-west of the house.

82
Design for Lady Scarsdale's Gown c.1770
anon
pen, sepia ink and watercolour
24 × 19

The range and diversity of the Kedleston drawings is shown by this charming design, probably for painted silk rather than embroidery, inscribed in pencil "Lady Scarsdale's purple Gown" and in sepia ink "The Star to be all Spangles, the Sattin to appear thro' where black'd". In 1770 Lady Scarsdale's dress account included one very costly item – "Mr Hinchliff Silk Mercer £234.16.3" – which may possibly be connected with this drawing.

Bibliography

Bolton: Arthur T. Bolton, *The Architecture of Robert and James Adam*, 1922

Bray: William Bray, *Tour into Derbyshire, etc.*, 1777

Coleridge: Anthony Coleridge, *Chippendale Furniture*, 1968

Colvin: H.M. Colvin, "Francis Smith of Warwick (1672–1738)", *Warwickshire History*, 2 (ii), 1972–73

Croft-Murray: Edward Croft-Murray, *Decorative Painting in England 1537–1837*, vol. 2, 1970

Fleming: John Fleming, *Robert Adam and His Circle*, 1962

Friedman: Terry Friedman, *James Gibbs*, 1984

Goodison: Nicholas Goodison, "Mr Stuart's Tripod", *Burlington Magazine*, 1972, 695–703

E. Harris: Eileen Harris, *The Furniture of Robert Adam*, 1963

J. Harris: John Harris, *The Artist and the Country House*, 1979

Hayward and Kirkham: Helena Hayward and Pat Kirkham, *William and John Linnell*, 1980

Oliver: ed. A. Oliver, *The Journal of Samuel Curwen, Loyalist*, Cambridge, Mass., 1972

Pottle: ed. F.A. Pottle, *The Private Papers of James Boswell*, 1937

Toynbee: ed. Paget Toynbee, "Horace Walpole's Journals of Visits to Country Seats", in *Walpole Society*, 16 (1927–28), 9–80

Watkin: David Watkin, *Athenian Stuart*, 1982

Willis: Peter Willis, *Charles Bridgeman and the English Landscape Garden*, 1977

Wilson: Gillian Wilson, "The Kedleston Fountain", *Journal of the J. Paul Getty Museum*, 11, 1983, 1–12

Photographic Acknowledgements

All photographs by Angelo Hornak except for those on pages 6–7 (National Trust); 7 – portrait of Mrs Garnett (Courtauld Institute of Art); 10–11 (*Country Life*); 25 – cat.no.10 (Leslie Harris); 33 (*Country Life*); 34 – platewarmer (National Trust); 37 – organ, 42 (*Country Life*); 58 (Geremy Butler); 62–63 – cat.no.48, 65, 66 (Black Box Studios); 68 (Courtauld Institute of Art); 73 – interior of stables, 81 – south front of Fishing Room (National Trust); 83 (Geremy Butler); 87 – hexagon temple (Derbyshire Life); 90 – Medicean lion (*Country Life*)